BIOLOGY

NOTES

COLES EDITORIAL BOARD

Bound to stay open

Publisher's Note

Otabind (Ota-bind). This book has been bound using the patented Otabind process. You can open this book at any page, gently run your finger down the spine, and the pages will lie flat.

ABOUT COLES NOTES

COLES NOTES have been an indispensible aid to students on five continents since 1948.

COLES NOTES are available for a wide range of individual literary works. Clear, concise explanations and insights are provided along with interesting interpretations and evaluations.

Proper use of COLES NOTES will allow the student to pay greater attention to lectures and spend less time taking notes. This will result in a broader understanding of the work being studied and will free the student for increased participation in discussions.

COLES NOTES are an invaluable aid for review and exam preparation as well as an invitation to explore different interpretive paths.

COLES NOTES are written by experts in their fields. It should be noted that any literary judgement expressed herein is just that – the judgement of one school of thought. Interpretations that diverge from, or totally disagree with any criticism may be equally valid.

COLES NOTES are designed to supplement the text and are not intended as a substitute for reading the text itself. Use of the NOTES will serve not only to clarify the work being studied, but should enhance the readers enjoyment of the topic.

ISBN 0-7740-3419-X

© COPYRIGHT 1998 AND PUBLISHED BY
COLES PUBLISHING COMPANY
TORONTO - CANADA
PRINTED IN CANADA

Manufactured by Webcom Limited
Cover finish: Webcom's Exclusive **DURACOAT**

CONTENTS

C O N T E N T S   (Continued)

CHARACTERISTICS OF LIVING THINGS

Definition of Life — No good definition of life exists. The difference between living and non-living things is recognized on the basis of the living thing exhibiting some or all of the following characteristics; movement, irritability, reproduction, metabolism.

MOVEMENT

All living protoplasm, plant and animal, is capable of some form of movement. In plants this is shown by tropisms, contractility, cell division, etc. Most animals, in addition to these activities, have the power of locomotion, they can move from place to place. This is an important advantage since it enables them to move into favorable environments.

A typical plant movement is the way growing stems will turn towards a source of light. This is because a much greater quantity of plant hormones, auxins, flows to the darker side of the stem. Auxins increase the growth of the plant cells on the darker side. The result of this unequal growth is that the longer side bends the stem over towards the light.

Some single-celled organisms, plant and animal, locomote by means of a whip-like flagellum e.g. *Euglena*.

Other unicellular animals are covered with thread-like cilia that move in a co-ordinated manner e.g. *Paramoecium*. The beating of the cilia causes the animal to move.

Multicellular animals have specialized muscle cells that are capable of contracting and moving the animal. In animals that lack definite skeletons, such as the earthworm and the octopus the muscles are arranged into two layers, a longitudinal layer and a circular layer. By contracting the circular muscles and relaxing the longitudinal muscles the part of the animal involved becomes long and thin. Contracting the longitudinal muscles and relaxing the circular ones causes shortening and thickening of the part in question. By combinations of these activities animals with this type of a structure can locomote. The digestive tract in mammals moves, but does not locomote, in a similar manner.

The most effective locomotion is observed when the muscular system acts in conjunction with a skeletal system. Muscles only work by contracting and so they usually are arranged in antagonistic pairs. While one member of a pair is in a state of contraction, the other usually is in a state of relaxation.

Vertebrate skeletal muscles rest upon the supporting bone and move the bones of the internal skeleton as a system of levers (usually third class levers), e.g. mammal, bird, reptile, frog, fish.

Invertebrate animals, e.g. crayfish and insects, have the skeleton outside the muscle system and arranged as a system of plates, rather like armour. The muscles are anchored to this exoskeleton and cause it to move.

IRRITABILITY

The property of protoplasm which enables it to respond to external stimuli, such as light, heat, touch, electricity, etc., is known as irritability. The responses of an animal, considered collectively, are called behavior. In the case of man this includes the emotions and the higher thought processes. In plants and simple animals, these responses are called tropisms. All living protoplasm is irritable and will respond to certain stimuli. Any change which may cause an organism to react is called a stimulus. The reaction is called a response.

The majority of responses (tropisms) of plants and of simpler animals are usually turning motions or growths in one particular direction. Movements toward a stimulus are called positive responses. Movements away from a stimulus are called negative responses.

CLASSIFICATION OF SOME TYPICAL TROPISMS

STIMULUS	NAME OF TROPISM	EXAMPLE
Light	Phototropism	plant leaves +
Water	Hydrotropism	plant roots +
Gravity	Geotropism	plant roots +
Chemicals	Chemotropism	hydra +
Touch	Thigmotropism	amoeba —
Heat	Thermotropism	amoeba —
Electricity	Galvanotropism	paramoecium —

More complex animals have special sense organs and these, in cooperation with a complicated nervous system allow these animals to respond to stimuli with greater accuracy. A particular sense organ or sense cell usually responds to only one kind of stimulus.

Sense organs can be classified according to their position:

1) Exteroceptors — Located at or near the surface of the body. Stimulated directly by external environmental changes. Subdivided into distance receptors e.g. the ear, eye and nose, and those that work on contact e.g. cutaneous receptors for pressure, pain and temperature.

2) Interoceptors — Located in the lining of the digestive tract and oral cavity e.g. taste receptors in the taste papilae on the surface of the tongue and receptors (probably reacting to pressure) in the stomach wall give rise to hunger feelings on stimulation.

3) Proprioceptors — Located within the body in regions other than the lining of the digestive tract. Stimulated directly by various chemical and physical processes of the body and only indirectly by changes occurring externally e.g. equilibrium receptors of the ear, the pain receptors of the internal organs and pressure receptors in muscles and joints.

REPRODUCTION

There are two types of reproduction — sexual and asexual. In sexual reproduction, two sex cells or gametes unite in fertilization to form a single cell known as a zygote. The zygote is the beginning of the life history of the new individual. In asexual reproduction, a part of a single parent, plant or animal, separates off and is capable of developing into an entire individual. There is no gamete production or fertilization.

Another method of asexual reproduction is vegetative propagation. This occurs when a portion of a living thing, not usually used for reproduction, gives rise to new organisms, e.g. the runners of strawberry plants, the tubers of potatoes, the rhizomes of iris, and the bulbs of tulips. Man makes use of vegetative propagation when he grafts branches of apple trees that bear desirable fruit on to the trunk of crab apple trees. The crab apple root and stem withstand the winter weather better than the root and stem of the original tree.

Sexual reproduction requires two cells or gametes, the nuclear material from these gametes combines and forms a single cell called a zygote. In lower organisms the gametes usually look alike. In higher organisms the gametes are unlike. One is called the male gamete or sperm, the other is called the female gamete or egg. In many plants and some animals both sperm and eggs are produced by the same individual, e.g. flowering plants, and the earthworm.

The single-celled zygote develops by cell division and differential growth into a new adult individual of the same species.

(See Figure 1)

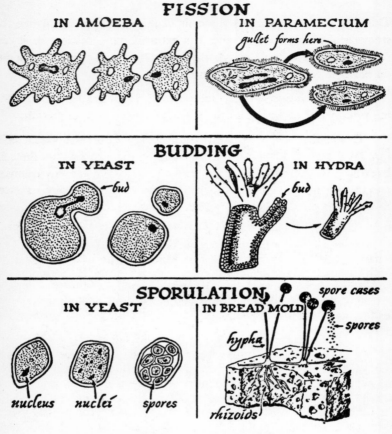

1. Various types of asexual reproduction.

METABOLISM

Metabolism is the total of all the chemical changes that take place in the protoplasm. It involves the following processes:

1) Photosynthesis — Takes place only in plants containing chlorophyll. Using the energy of the sun, carbon dioxide and water are combined to produce glucose and molecular oxygen.

$$6\,CO_2 + 6\,H_2O \longrightarrow C_6H_{12}O_6 + 6\,O_2$$

2) Digestion — The alteration of food (usually by the action of enzymes) into chemical units that can be absorbed by the organism.

This can take place outside the cells of the organism, e.g. inside the stomach of man, in which case it is extracellular digestion, or it can take place in a vacuole inside a cell in which case it is intracellular digestion, e.g. food vacuole in *amoeba*.

3) Assimilation — The incorporation of materials into the living protoplasm of an organism. Closely associated with growth.

4) Respiration — The release of energy within individual cells through the breakdown of energy-containing chemicals within the cell. Breathing is the exchange of O_2 and CO_2 between the environment and the organism. In multicellular organisms there is usually a system to transport the O_2 and CO_2 within the organism.

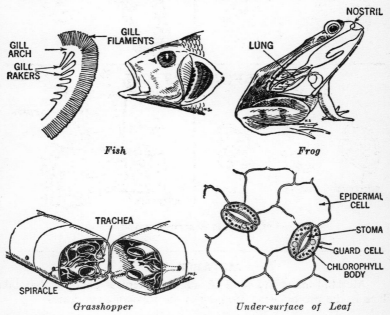

2.   Gas exchange organs or four representative organisms.

5) Excretion — The separation, from the living protoplasm of the organism, of the waste products of metabolism. Water, CO_2, salts and various nitrogen-containing molecules are excreted.

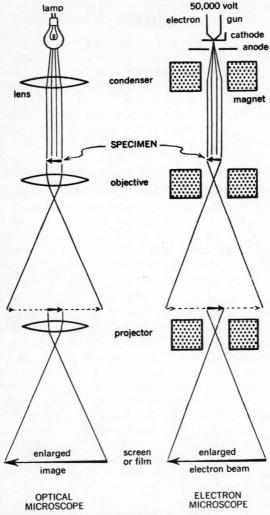

lamp

50,000 volt
electron gun
cathode
anode

lens
condenser
magnet

SPECIMEN

objective

projector

enlarged
image
screen
or film
enlarged
electron beam

OPTICAL
MICROSCOPE

ELECTRON
MICROSCOPE

3. OPTICAL MICROSCOPE (inverted). Light beam from lamp concentrated by condenser lens to illuminate specimen; image focused and magnified by objective, and again by projector (eyepiece); enlarged image seen on viewing screen or photographed on film. **ELECTRON MICROSCOPE.** Narrow beam of high speed electrons from cathode passes through hole in anode and is concentrated by doughnut-shaped magnetic coil (condenser) to pass through specimen; emerging electron pattern focused and magnifed (2d magnet) and further enlarged (3d magnet); "image either seen on fluorescent screen or recorded on film. Entire instrument enclosed in high vacuum because electrons are scattered in air.

CELLS

Most cells are very small and consequently must be greatly magnified if their structure is to be studied. The major limiting factor in studying small structures is the limit of resolution of the human eye. Resolution, in optics, is the minimum separation of two objects at which they appear distinct and separate. The human eye can resolve objects 1/10 mm. apart. Closer than 1/10 mm. the objects blend and look like only one. Because of the small size of cell structures, millimeters are too large a unit and A^{0}ngstrom units (A^0) are used. An A^{0}ngstrom unit is equal to 1×10^7 mm. The resolving power of the unaided human eye is therefore 1×10^6 A^0 or 1,000,000 A^0.

The lenses of a light microscope spread the beams of light coming from objects and therefore can increase resolution by making objects appear farther apart. The limit of resolution of the light microscope is approximately half the wavelength of the light used for illumination. Since white light with an average wavelength of 5500 A^0 is usually used, resolution is about 2750 A^0 or about 400 times better than that of the eye alone.

The electron microscope uses beams of electrons in place of light and a system of magnets to focus these beams of electrons in place of the glass lenses found in a light microscope. This entire system must work in a vacuum. Electron microscopes now being used give a resolution of 10 A^0 about 250 times better than that obtained with the light microscope. Instead of spreading beams of visible light, the electron miscroscope spreads electrons. The image can be made visible by use of a fluorescent screen or it can be recorded on a photographic plate. The images seen result from the electrons being selectively dispersed by the object being viewed. Some structures will absorb electrons more than others. The material being viewed must be dead since it could not live in the vacuum or the electron beam of the instrument, and the object to be viewed must be very thin because of the low penetrating power of the electron beam.

CELL STRUCTURE

There are no "average" cells. The illustrations that follow show structures that are usually seen in plant and animal cells.

The principal differences between plant and animal cells are:

1) Plant cells are usually larger, with distinct outlines and have a cellulose cell wall. Animal cells have cell membranes but no cell walls and do not contain cellulose.

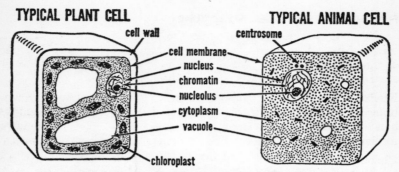

TYPICAL PLANT CELL   **TYPICAL ANIMAL CELL**

cell wall

centrosome

cell membrane
nucleus
chromatin
nucleolus
cytoplasm
vacuole

chloroplast

4.   Comparison of typical plant and animal cells, diagrammatic.

2) Mature plant cells have only a thin lining of cytoplasm with a large central vacuole. Animal cells have continuous cytoplasm, if vacuoles are present they are usually small.

3) Most plant cells contain chloroplasts and are capable of photosynthesis. Animal cells do not contain chlorophyll and cannot photosynthesize.

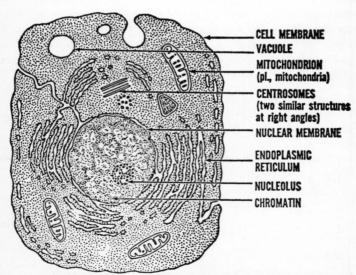

CELL MEMBRANE
VACUOLE
MITOCHONDRION
(pl., mitochondria)
CENTROSOMES
(two similar structures
at right angles)
NUCLEAR MEMBRANE
ENDOPLASMIC
RETICULUM
NUCLEOLUS
CHROMATIN

5.   Fine structure of a typical animal cell as revealed by the
electron microscope.

FUNCTIONS OF THE CELL STRUCTURES —

1) The nucleus — essential to the life of the cell. Contains a special kind of protoplasm, chromatin material, from which the chromosomes will form during cell division. It also contains one or more nucleoli and has a definite membrane.

Nuclear membrane — has a structure similar to that of the cell membrane as shown in figure 6. Regulates the movement of materials between the nucleus and the cytoplasm. It does not act passively or mechanically like a sieve but actively controls the traffic of chemicals.

Chromosomes — structures formed during cell division from the chromatin material of the nucleus. The chromosomes contain DNA molecules which carry an encoded description of the entire organism. The action of this DNA ultimately controls all long-term cell activities.

Nucleolus — Contains very large amounts of RNA. Probably plays a role in protein synthesis in cells. Has no limiting membrane.

2) The cytoplasm — a complex fluid mixture containing and surrounding the various cellular organells such as mitochondria, endoplasmic reticulum, etc. Cytoplasm consists of water, proteins and lipids in colloidal solution, nucleic acids, salts and pigments. The structure of cytoplasm is unknown, it frequently exhibits streaming movements. It provides the environment and many of the raw materials for the actions of the cell organells.

The cell membrane or unit membrane — typically a double layered structure 75 A⁰ thick consisting of a protein-lipid-lipid-protein sequence.

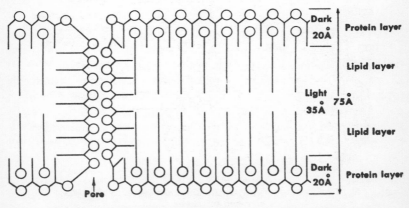

6. A model of the molecular structure of a limiting membrane.

All cell membranes, the nuclear membrane and the membranes surrounding most cell organells have this basic structure. The cell membrane selectively regulates the passage of dissolved substances and water into and out of the cell. All substances which enter or leave the cell must pass through the cell membrane.

Endoplasmic reticulum (ER) — consists of two unit membranes separated by a fluid-filled space. This is arranged in a net-like structure (a reticulum) that fills the cytoplasmic space stretching from the cell membrane to the nuclear membrane. The Golgi apparatus is a special part of this structure. Sometimes the space between the two unit membranes forms rounded structures called cisternae (or little jugs). ER may have ribosomes, small electron-dense granules, on its surface, in which case it is called "rough ER" or it may lack ribosomes in which case it is called "smooth ER". When cells are making proteins the amount of "rough ER" is usually high. The endoplasmic reticulum increases the interior surface of the cell enormously and provides a structure on which organized enzymatic activity can occur.

Golgi apparatus — consists of many layers of unit membranes stacked on one another. The function of this apparatus is not definitely known. Secretory cells typically have large Golgi apparatus and it may play a role in the storage and/or synthesis of secretory products.

Ribosomes — Particles 150 to 200 A^0 in size consisting of RNA and protein in approximately equal amounts. Closely associated with some types of endoplasmic reticulum forming "rough ER" ribosomes act during the synthesis of proteins by cells. Ribosomes are sometimes called microsomes by biochemists.

Mitochondria — Round or sausage-shaped organells 5,000 to 100,000 A^0 long. The outer surface is formed by a double unit membrane. The inner unit membrane is thrown up into a series of shelf-like folds or cristae. The mitochondria hold the enzymes responsible for aerobic cellular respiration in which molecules containing 3 carbon units are oxidized to CO_2 and water. Much of the energy produced by this controlled oxidation is stored in molecules of adenosine triphosphate (ATP). ATP can be considered a "storage battery" for living reactions.

Lysosomes — Sphere-like structures in the cytoplasm that have a definite membrane. Contains high concentration of digestive (hydrolysing) enzymes that can hydrolize large molecules, e.g. fat, proteins,

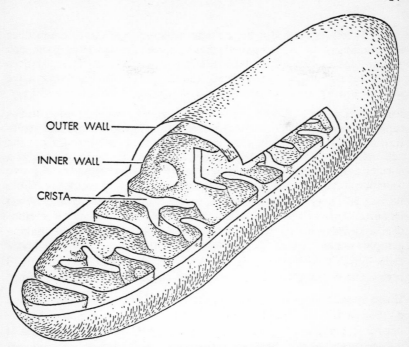

OUTER WALL

INNER WALL

CRISTA

7. Structure of Mitochondrion is basically that of a fluid filled vessel with an involuted wall. The wall consists of a double unit membrane.

carbohydrates. If the limiting membrane is damaged these enzymes will digest (autolyse) the entire structure of the cell.

Centrosome — A spherical structure found in all animal cells and some plant cells. It contains two centrioles, complex cylindrical structures which form the poles of the mitotic spindle during cell division.

Plastids — Round or oval bodies found in plant cells, classified on the basis of color. Colorless leucoplasts are used for storing starch. Chromoplasts store pigments of various colors. Green chloroplasts are highly organized, multi-layered structures containing chlorophyll found in green plant cells and are the centres of photosynthesis in such cells.

Vacuoles — Droplets of liquid in the cytoplasm surrounded by a membrane. Vacuoles serve as storage, transport and processing centres in the cytoplasm.

COMPOSITION OF PROTOPLASM

Protoplasm, the living substance within cells is an extremely complicated association of chemicals. These chemicals are arranged as mixtures, solutions, colloidal suspensions, crystals and highly ordered solids. The activities of protoplasm, so far studied by scientific method, have been explained on the basis of the chemical and physical properties of the atoms and molecules which constitute the protoplasm.

PHYSICAL PROPERTIES OF PROTOPLASM

Physically, protoplasm is best thought of as a colloid, a liquid system containing particles which are too large to dissolve and too small to settle out. Colloids can exist in two physical states, as a sol and as a gel. In the sol state, the solid colloidal particles are surrounded by water and consequently will move as a liquid. In the gel state, the colloidal particles touch one another trapping the water between them; this semi-solid will not move as a liquid but rather resembles jelly.

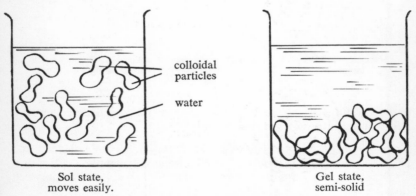

colloidal particles

water

Sol state, moves easily.

Gel state, semi-solid

8.   Two physical states of colloidal suspensions, diagrammatic.

Protoplasmic colloids can undergo reversible sol-gel transformations. The *amoeba* is thought to move by changing the protoplasm at the tip of a pseudopod into a sol and then causing sol-state protoplasm to flow into this area by having gel-state protoplasm form at the back of the animal, pushing the sol-state protoplasm forward.

Protoplasm in all living cells is constantly moving; this helps distribute the products of cell metabolism throughout the cell. This protoplasmic movement can be caused by local sol-gel transformation or by thermal agitation of molecules in the protoplasm.

Protoplasm is unstable and maintains its organization by continuous use of energy obtained from metabolic processes that are constantly occurring in every cell.

REVIEW OF CHEMICAL BACKGROUND:

Atoms — All matter can be thought to consist of atoms; the atoms of any element, e.g. oxygen, are different from the atoms of all others. It is the unique structure of atoms which gives each element its unique characteristcis. There are 92 naturally occurring elements; 27 of these are natural constituents of protoplasm, e.g. carbon, hydrogen, oxygen, nitrogen, sulphur, phosphorus.

An atom can be considered to have a central nucleus consisting of positively-charged protons and neutral neutrons. For every proton

HYDROGEN ATOM

Atomic number = 1
Atomic weight = 1

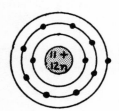

SODIUM ATOM

Atomic Number = 11
Atomic Weight = 23

Electrons — 2, 8, 1

CHLORINE ATOM

Atomic Number = 17
Atomic Weight = 35

Electrons — 2, 8, 7

9.   Diagrams of atoms, the nucleus is shaded, the protons are indicated by +, the neutrons by n, and the electrons by ●.

in the nucleus there is a negative electron orbiting around the nucleus. The electrons orbit in definite layers or electron shells and each shell will hold a characteristic number of electrons.

Counting out from the nucleus, the 1st shell will hold 2 electrons, the 2nd, 8 electrons, the 3rd, 8 , and the 4th, 18 electrons. It is the electrons in the outermost electron shell which are involved in chemical reactions. Atoms can gain, lose or share electrons with other atoms and this is the very basis of all life processes.

Molecules — A molecule is a combination of two or more atoms. These constituent atoms are held together by chemical bonds. Chemical reactions between atoms result from the tendency of atoms to achieve a stable configuration of electrons in their outer electron shell.

Chemical bonds — There are two major types.

1) Ionic or electrovalent bond, found mostly in inorganic compounds characterized by one atom giving up its outermost electrons to one or more other atoms e.g. sodium giving up one electron to chlorine to form sodium chloride.

2) Covalent bond, found mostly in organic compounds, characterized by the sharing of one or more pairs of electrons between atoms e.g. four atoms of hydrogen sharing electrons with one atom of carbon to form methane.

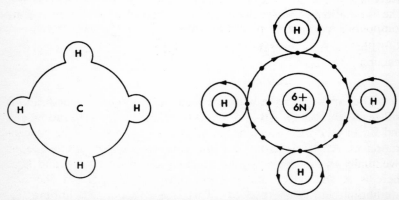

10.   The covalent bond in methane, a carbon compound of one central carbon atom and four surrounding hydrogen atoms. Each atom shares electrons possessed by atoms of the other element.

Both types of chemical bond contain energy. All chemical reactions involve an exchange of energy. Some chemical bonds contain more energy than others e.g. when a carbon-to-hydrogen bond, such as found in methane, is broken, more energy is released than when a carbon-to-carbon bond is broken. Living organisms store most of their chemical potential energy in special high energy bonds of a chemical known as adenosine triphosphate (ATP) which is composed of a molecule of adenosine to which two phosphate groups are attached by means of high energy bonds.

Energy changes associated with chemical reactions — Chemical reactions can be divided into two classes on the basis of energy exchange:

    1) Exergonic reactions, release more energy than they absorb e.g. cellular respiration.

    2) Endergonic reactions, absorb more energy than they release e.g. photosynthesis.

    Both types of reaction require a small extra amount of energy to start the reaction. This has been called the energy of activation.

Ionization — An ion is an atom that carries an electrical charge, e.g. if solid sodium chloride is dissolved in water, the sodium separates away from the chlorine but leaves behind the electron it has given up to chlorine when it formed molecular sodium chloride. In this way the sodium atom has lost a negative charge and has become a positively charged ion, similarly the chlorine ion gained a negative charge. The separation of molecules into ions is called dissociation. Many compounds ionize when placed in water.

Equilibrium in chemical reactions — Suppose we have the reversible reaction

$$A + B \rightleftharpoons AB$$

    The arrows going in both directions $\rightleftharpoons$ indicate that A and B will react to produce AB and that AB wil break down to produce A and B. In a closed system as A and B react to form AB the concentration of A and B drops and the concentration of AB increases. Eventually as much AB will be breaking down to form A and B as there is A and B reacting to form AB. At this point a chemical equilibrium has been reached. This is a dynamic equilibrium; although the relative concentrations of A and B and AB do not change, AB is continuously breaking down to form A and B and A and B are continuously reacting to form AB. If some AB is removed from the reaction, the direction of the reaction will shift to the right.

$$A + B \; \underrightarrow{\xleftarrow{}} \; AB \text{ (some AB removed)}$$

If AB is added the reaction will shift to the left

$$A + B \; \overleftarrow{\underrightarrow{}} \; AB + AB$$

but only the direction and rate of the reaction will shift.

Most chemical reactions in living systems are reversible and exist in a state of dynamic equilibrium, however most chemical reactions in living organisms are very complex and the products of one reaction form the reactants for the next reaction, e.g.

$$A + B \; \underrightarrow{\xleftarrow{}} \; AB + CD \; \underrightarrow{\xleftarrow{}} \; ABCD \; \underrightarrow{\xleftarrow{}} \; ABD + C \nearrow$$

if C is given off as a gas, as CO_2 is from living organisms, there will be a continuous removal from one side of the reaction which will keep the entire reaction shifting to the right.

If the reaction $ABCD \; \underrightarrow{\xleftarrow{}} \; ABD + C \nearrow$ releases energy, such as when glucose is broken down to form CO_2 and H_2O, again the equilibrium will be shifted to the right.

Catalysts — Catalysts are chemical substances which change the *rate* of a chemical reaction and emerge from the reaction chemically unchanged. *Enzymes* are protein molecules that act as catalysts in living systems. The enzyme has a special surface that attracts the reactants and lines them up so they can react. Once the reaction has taken place the products of the reaction are repelled from the enzyme surface and it is free to attract more reactants. In living organisms enzymes usually speed up the chemical reactions.

Organic Molecules — Carbon, hydrogen, oxygen and nitrogen make up about 96 per cent of the total weight of protoplasm. The so-called "organic" molecules were so named because at one time it was thought that they could only be made by living organisms. Organic molecules are all carbon compounds. Carbon, with a valence of 4 can link up in many different ways and can form long chains and rings. There are 4 main classes of organic compounds found in living organisms — carbohydrates, fats, proteins and nucleic acids.

   1) Carbohydrates — (sugars, starch, cellulose, glycogen). General formula $C_n(H_2O)_n$ e.g. glucose $C_6(H_2O)_6$ or $C_6H_{12}O_6$. The only elements present in carbohydrates are carbon, oxygen and hydrogen. Two sugars can join together to form a disaccharide or many sugars can join together to form polysaccharides. The sugar units join in such a way that a molecule of H_2O is excluded. The exact way that the sugar units join together can have an effect on whether or not they can be digested. For example, both starch and cellulose are long polymers of glucose sugar units but the glucose to glucose linkages are different. We can digest starch because we have enzymes that will insert H_2O molecules between its glucose units thus breaking the bonds. The bonds of cellulose resist digestion. Carbohydrates provide most of the chemical energy required by living organisms.

2) Fats — (lipids). All fats have a similar general structure which consists of glycerol, a 3 carbon alcohol, and three fatty acids.

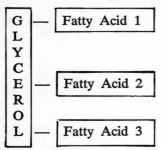

Differences between fat molecules depend on differences in the constituent fatty acids.

A fatty acid is a long chain carbon compound ending in a carboxyl group (COOH). It is the carboxyl group which makes this compound an acid.

$$\begin{array}{ccccccccc}
 & H & & H & & H & & H & & & & H & & H \\
 & | & & | & & | & & | & & & & | & & | \\
H- & C & - & C & - & C & - & C & \text{- - - - - -} & C & - & C & - & C & = O \\
 & | & & | & & | & & | & & & & | & & | \\
 & H & & H & & H & & H & & & & H & & H & & OH
\end{array}$$

When fats are digested the chemical bond between the glycerol molecule and each fatty acid molecule is broken by having a molecule of H_2O inserted. Fat molecules contain a large amount of potential chemical energy because of their large number of carbon to hydrogen bonds. Certain fatty acids e.g. linoleic acid are "essential" — we cannot make them, they must be supplied in the diet.

3) Proteins — Proteins consist of long chains of amino acids joined together by special chemical bonds; peptide bonds. Proteins are important as structural units of protoplasm and as enzymes, the organic catalysts which facilitate most of the chemical reactions which take place in living organisms.

There are about 22 different kinds of amino acids found in protein molecules. Amino acids have a characteristic structure. Structure of an amino acid:

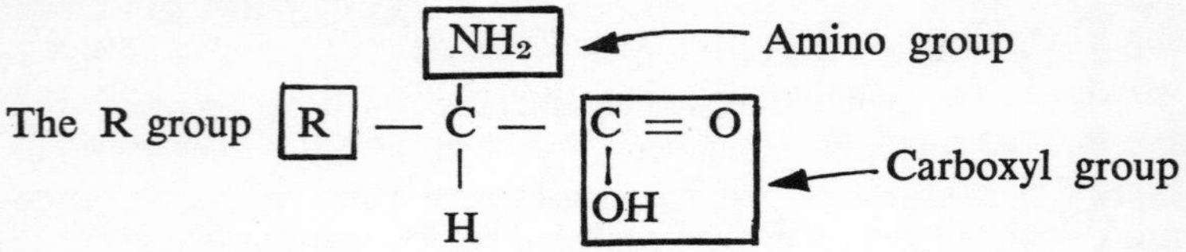

The R group $\boxed{R}$ — $\underset{H}{\overset{\boxed{NH_2}}{C}}$ — $\boxed{C = O \atop OH}$

— Amino group

— Carboxyl group

The R-group can be any of 22 different carbon chains. It is in the arrangement of the atoms in the R-group that amino acids differ from one another.

The carboxyl group (COOH) gives the molecule its acid properties; this is the same group as one finds in fatty acids.

The amino group (NH₂) gives a basic reaction. Amino acids are linked together by peptide bonds.

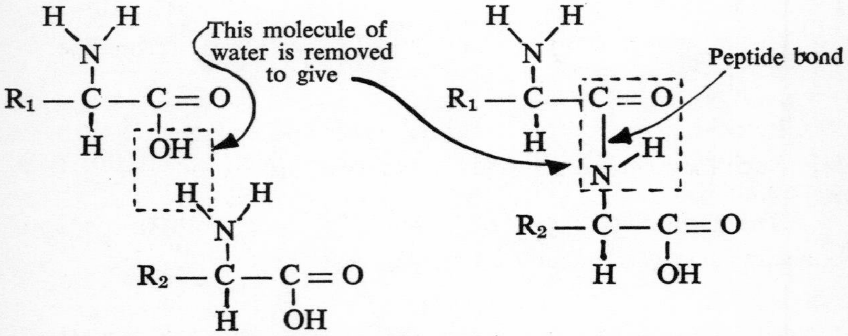

This molecule of water is removed to give

Peptide bond

Proteins are very complex substances with complex relationships between their sub-units.

amino acid + amino acid = dipeptide

dipeptide + dipeptide = polypeptide

polypeptide + polypeptide = protein (50 to 2000 amino acids)

A great many different kinds of proteins are made by cells. If one thinks of the 22 amino acids as letters of an alphabet one can appreciate that a great many different 50 to 2000 letter "words" or protein molecules could be constructed.

4) Nucleic Acids — Very complicated molecules first isolated from cell nuclei. Nucleic acids are long chains of nucleotide molecules. A nucleotide consists of 3 molecules joined together, a 5-carbon sugar, a phosphate group (PO_4) and a nitrogen-containing compound which can be either a purine or a pyrimidine.

(PO_4) — | 5 Carbon Sugar | — | Purine or Pyrimidine |

Each sugar can form bonds with 2 (P) groups and thus a long chain can be formed

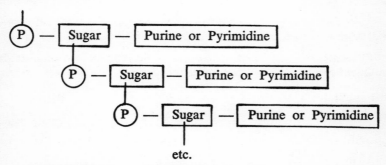

etc.

Such long chains are called polynucleotides.

There are 2 main types of nucleic acids found in cells: deoxyribonucleic acid (DNA) and ribonucleic acid (RNA).

TABLE 1
COMPARISON BETWEEN DNA AND RNA

	DNA	RNA
Sugar	deoxyribose	ribose
Phosphate	phosphate	phosphate
Purines	adenine, guanine	adenine, guanine
Pyrimidines	cytosine, thymine	cytosine, uracil

Pyrimidines are smaller than purines and have only one ring, e.g. cytosine.

Purines are larger and have two rings, e.g. adenine.

Nucleic acids play an important role in genetics and protein synthesis and will be discussed in more detail in a later section.

CATABOLISM

A general term to describe metabolic processes which release energy, e.g. digestion and cellular respiration.

Digestion — alteration of food (usually by enzymes) into simpler units which can be absorbed into the living protoplasm.

Structure of Digestive System in Man — This system includes the alimentary canal (digestive tract) and several glands (liver, pancreas, salivary glands).

ALIMENTARY CANAL —

Mouth — fleshy lips; teeth; hard and soft palates; tongue — muscular, taste buds, mucous glands; saliva ducts on sides of cheeks and under tongue; pharynx (behind soft palate) contains mucous glands, tonsils, adenoids, nasal openings, eustachian tube openings, glottis (covered by epiglottis) and gullet opening.

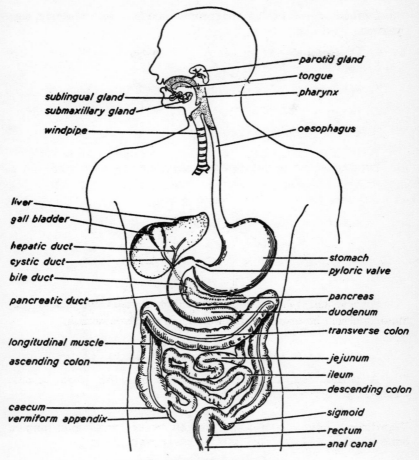

parotid gland
tongue
pharynx
oesophagus

sublingual gland
submaxillary gland
windpipe

liver
gall bladder

hepatic duct
cystic duct
bile duct

pancreatic duct

longitudinal muscle
ascending colon

caecum
vermiform appendix

stomach
pyloric valve

pancreas
duodenum
transverse colon

jejunum
ileum
descending colon

sigmoid
rectum
anal canal

11. The human digestive system.

Gullet — (oesophagus) — a muscular tube with wall of four layers (same as stomach and intestinal walls) (fibrous coat, muscle layer, sub-mucosa, and mucosa); mucosa secretes mucus for lubrication.

Stomach — left side below diaphragm, 1½ quart capacity; muscle layer has fibres in 3 directions — circular, longitudinal and oblique — for mechanical mixing activity; gastric glands in mucosa; pyloric valve at lower end. Layers of peritoneum (mesenteries) support stomach, nerves and blood vessels.

Small intestine — 23 feet from pylorus to large intestine; three sections may be distinguished:

1) Duodenum — 11 inches x 2 inches diameter — first loop next to stomach; has openings from pancreatic and bile ducts.

2) Jejunum — 8 feet x slightly less than 2 inches diameter.

3) Ileum — 13 feet, coiled, thinner walls, 1½ inch diameter; has valve where it joins large intestine.

Walls of small intestine have about 5 million tiny projections called villi, also circular folds to increase surface area. A villus has a single layer epithelium, connective tissue, capillary and lacteal. Intestinal glands between villi secrete intestinal juice.

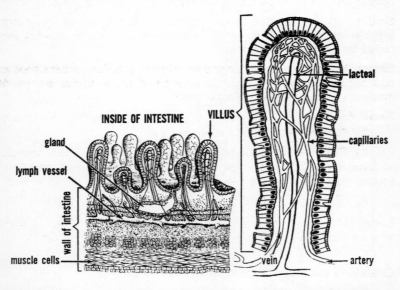

12. Villi of the small intestine. The diagram at lower left also shows the muscle cells of the intestinal wall, an intestinal gland, and a lymph vessel to which the lacteals are connected.

Large Intestine — 5 feet x 2½ inches diameter; no villi or circular folds; consists of ascending, transverse and descending colons; cecum and appendix where it joins small intestine; at lower end rectum and anus.

DIGESTIVE GLANDS OUTSIDE THE ALIMENTARY CANAL

1) Liver — dark red, lobed, below diaphragm on right side; secretes bile that is then stored in gall bladder; bile duct to duodenum.

2) Pancreas — grey, 7 inches long, between stomach and duodenum; secretes pancreatic juice by pancreatic duct to bile duct to duodenum.

3) Salivary glands — 3 pairs — parotid (below ears), sub-maxillary (under lower jaws) and sub-lingual (under tongue); ducts take saliva into mouth.

MECHANICAL PROCESSES OF DIGESTION

Mouth — Food is broken up by teeth, moistened by saliva, rolled back by tongue into pharynx which pushes it into gullet opening.

Gullet — peristalsis pushes food down gullet, moistened by mucus; a peristaltic wave is a wave of constriction of circular muscles preceded by a wave of relaxation.

Stomach — peristalsis in lower part; churning action; breaks food up and mixes with gastric juice; two to three hours action for solids; produces a creamy mass called chyme.

Small Intestine —

1) Peristalsis moves food along.

2) Rhythmical segmentation — contraction of circular muscles at intervals — followed by relaxation and constriction at middle of former segments —mixes food with digestive juices.

3) Waving of villi — mixing.

Large Intestine — mass peristalsis two or three times a day to move waste material along; some rhythmical segmentation may occur.

CHEMICAL PROCESSES OF DIGESTION

Brought about by enzymes (organic catalysts) present in digestive juices which act by inserting molecules of H_2O at specific chemical linkages. This breaking up of large food molecules, starch, fats and proteins, into smaller units, is called hydrolysis.

Mouth — amylase (ptyalin) in saliva begins change of starch to maltose sugar; alkaline reaction; uncooked starch grains not digested because of cellulose covering on starch grains.

Stomach — gastric juice contains several enzymes:

1) **pepsin** — changes proteins to polypeptides.

2) **rennin** — in mammal stomachs, curdles milk — e.g. coagulates the milk protein (casein) so that pepsin can digest it.

3) **lipase** — breaks down already emulsified fats (milk fat and egg yolk fat) to fatty acid and glycerol; other fats liquefied by body temperature.

Hydrochloric acid in gastric juice converts proteins to jelly-like mass, — gives stomach contents an acid reaction so pepsin can work, dissolves minerals and kills bacteria.

A hormone, **gastrin,** is produced in stomach when stimulated by food — this causes gastric glands to produce gastric juice.

Liver — produces bile — stored in gall bladder, then sent to duodenum; alkaline — neutralizes acid from stomach; bile salts emulsify fats to give larger surface for enzyme action; bile pigment — (reddish yellow) — is from waste part of haemoglobin from worn out red blood cells; no enzymes in bile.

Pancreas — produces pancreatic juice which has 4 important enzymes — enters duodenum by bile duct —

1) **trypsin** — changes large polypeptides to smaller ones.

2) **amylopsin** — changes starch to maltose.

3) **steapsin** — (pancreatic lipase) — changes fats to fatty acids and glycerol.

4) **carboxypeptidase** — takes amino acids off polypeptides from the carboxyl group end of the molecule.

Secretin — a hormone produced in the intestine when food is present, stimulates liver and pancreas to produce their juices.

Small Intestine — intestinal glands produce intestinal juice containing 6 enzymes —

1) **dipeptidase** (erepsin) — changes dipeptides to amino acids.

2) **amino-peptidase** — takes amino acids off polpeptides from the amino group end of the molecule.

3) **intestinal lipase** — changes fats to fatty acids and glycerol.

4) **maltase** — changes maltose to glucose.

5) **lactase** — changes lactose (milk sugar) to glucose.

6) **sucrase** — changes sucrose (cane sugar) to glucose and fructose.

ABSORPTION OF DIGESTED FOOD

1) Stomach — water, alcohol, simple sugars (glucose etc.) are absorbed through the cells lining the stomach into gastric capillaries.

2) Small Intestine — chief absorbing region; amino acids, glucose, vitamins, minerals, water are absorbed through the lining cells into blood in capillaries in villi; fatty acids and glycerin pass into epithelial cells of villi, recombine to form fat and then pass into lymph lacteals — bile salts assist fat absorption.

3) Large Intestine — water is absorbed from remaining undigested material.

TRANSPORTATION OF FOOD IN THE BODY —

From the villi capillaries absorbed food goes by hepatic portal vein to liver where some is temporarily stored, the rest is carried by the blood system to cells in all parts of body for use. Fats go from villi lacteals through lymph system to thoracic duct where they pass into the blood system and are then carried to all parts of body for use.

FOOD TRANSPORTATION CAN BE SUMMARIZED AS FOLLOWS:

1) Blood carries glucose, amino acids, fats, vitamins, minerals.

2) Lymph lacteals carry fats to blood system.

3) Lymph as tissue fluid carries glucose, fats, amino acids, vitamins and minerals from blood capillaries to tissue cells.

THE USE OF DIGESTED AND ABSORBED FOOD —

Food units are used by the body in 3 ways:

1) As a source of "building blocks" to allow protoplasm to grow and repair itself.

2) As a source of special chemicals, vitamins, essential amino acids, essential fatty acids, which the organism requires for function but cannot make itself.

3) As a source of energy to allow the protoplasm to maintain its high degree of organization. Living cells release this energy through a process known as cellular respiration.

RESPIRATION —

A cellular function that should not be confused with breathing or gas exchange. Complex chemical molecules e.g. glucose, which contain large amounts of chemical potential energy in their chemical bonds, have these bonds systematically broken. Enzymes are used to break the bonds and the energy that is released is transferred, through a system of carrier chemicals, to a "high energy bond" in which a phosphate group ⓟ is added to adenosine diphosphate (ADP) to form adenosine triphosphate (ATP).

$$ADP + ⓟ + energy \longrightarrow ATP$$

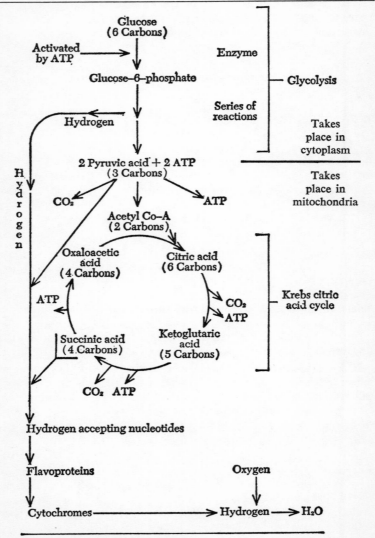

ATP is formed in these reactions.

13. **Chemical pathways in cellular respiration.**

The efficiency of this energy trapping system is about 67 per cent. The rest of the energy is lost as heat. This heat is used to help maintain the body temperature but is not available for work.

The general reaction for cellular respiration is

$$C_6H_{12}O_6 + 6\ O_2 \xrightarrow{\text{enzymes}} 6\ CO_2 + 6\ H_2O + \text{Energy (ATP)}$$

Although cellular respiration is usually thought of as the oxidation of glucose this oxidation is accomplished by the removal of atoms of hydrogen not by the addition of oxygen. The oxygen is used to trap the hydrogens that result when carbon to hydrogen chemical bonds are broken. This forms water (H_2O) one of the byproducts of respiration. The carbon from the carbon to hydrogen bonds are given off as CO_2.

The various steps in cellular respiration are summarized in figure 13.

Fat and protein molecules can also be used for cellular respiration.

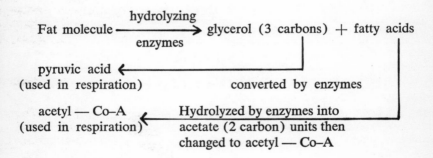

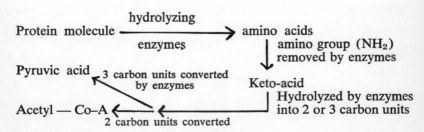

Uses of ATP Energy — When ATP releases the energy of its high energy phosphate bond about 12,000 calories of energy are made available to the cell. Some of the ways this energy is used are listed below:

1) For muscle contraction.

2) To provide energy for endothermic chemical reactions such as the synthesis of proteins, glycogen, hormones and other metabolic chemicals (most chemical reactions that take place in cells are endothermic).

3) To provide energy for the active transport of substances moving against concentration gradients.

4) To maintain the complex organization of living protoplasm.

Metabolic Role of Vitamins — Vitamins are chemicals required in small amounts for metabolism. Most of them work with enzymes as coenzymes. They are essential dietary factors since our bodies cannot make them.

TABLE 2
METABOLIC ROLE OF CERTAIN VITAMINS

VITAMIN	CHIEF FUNCTIONS	EFFECTS OF DEFICIENCY
A	chemistry of vision, maintains cell membranes	night blindness lowered resistance to infection
B_1 thiamine	essential for growth, normal functioning of nerves, acts in cell respiration	beri-beri in man polyneuritis in animals
B_2 riboflavin	acts as part of hydrogen carrier system in cell respiration	growth retarded eye defects
nicotinic acid	acts as part of coenzymes in cell respiration	pellagra
pantothenic acid	forms part of coenzyme A which functions with acetate units during cell respiration	retarded growth
folic acid	acts in the metabolism of nucleic acids	anemia, abnormal growth

B_{12}	acts in the metabolism of nucleic acids	anemia, abnormal growth
biotin	metabolism of one-carbon compounds, e.g. CO_2.	skin and bones abnormal
choline	acts in fat and protein metabolism	hemorrhages, abnormal growth
B_6 pyriodoxine	acts in fat and protein metabolism	retarded growth
C ascorbic acid	acts in the oxidation of amino acids	scurvy, connective tissue degeneration
D calciferol	helps regulate calcium and phosphorous deposits in bones	rickets, abnormal bone development

Metabolic Role of Minerals — Minerals are also important in metabolism and many of them are essential nutrients.

TABLE 3
METABOLIC ROLE OF SOME IMPORTANT MINERALS

MINERAL	CHIEF FUNCTIONS
Iron	essential part of haemoglobin molecule and certain other enzymes that act in cellular respiration
Sodium	sodium ions are used in the conduction of nerve impulses; helps maintain normal osmotic balance of blood; a structural part of bone
Chlorine	helps maintain ionic balance of blood; adjusts electrical charges on red blood cells
Calcium	part of bone structure; acts in blood clotting
Potassium	acts in conduction of nerve impulses; is essential for growth
Phosphorous	required for phosphate groups in ATP and nucleic acids; a structural part of proteins, nervous tissue and bone
Sulphur (Sulfur)	found in many proteins; a structural part of certain amino acids
Iodine	required for the production of thyroxin by the thyroid gland

ANABOLISM

Metabolic processes which trap energy, e.g. photosynthesis; or lead to the formation of complex molecules in living organisms, e.g. the synthesis of cellulose, glycogen, fats and proteins.

Photosynthesis — The synthesis of glucose from carbon dioxide and water, by cells which contain chlorophyll.

$$6 \ CO_2 + 6 \ H_2O \xrightarrow[\text{light energy}]{\text{chlorophyll}} C_6H_{12}O_6 + 6 \ O_2 \nearrow$$

This is an endergonic (energy-demanding) reaction and the energy comes from the sun. Chlorophyll has the ability to trap part of the energy of sunlight and become "activated chlorophyll". "Activated chlorophyll", in conjunction with very elaborate systems of enzymes, is able to pass this energy on and it is used to form carbon to carbon bonds, carbon to hydrogen bonds and finally, after many steps, glucose is formed. The potential chemical energy stored in the chemical bonds of the sugar molecule can be used in respiration. Molecular oxygen is a very important by-product of photosynthesis.

Chloroplasts — The chlorophyll in plants is not loose in the cytoplasm, but is arranged in special organelles called chloroplasts. The chlorophyll molecules in chloroplasts are stacked in layers between other layers of lipoid (fat-like) molecules and protein molecules (which can act as enzymes).

Photosynthesis is an extremely complex reaction involving many steps, each step catalyzed by a specific enzyme.

SUMMARY OF PHOTOSYNTHESIS

1) Chlorophyll molecules trap energy from sunlight.

2) This energy is transferred to the ADP-ATP energy system which is linked to enzymes that can cause step 3.

3) This energy is used to split water (H_2O) into hydrogen atoms and molecular oxygen.

$$2 \ H_2O \longrightarrow O_2 \nearrow + 4 \ H^+$$

This is called the photolysis of water. The molecular O_2 is released to the atmosphere and the hydrogens are trapped by a series of molecules that can act as hydrogen carriers.

4) The hydrogen and carrier molecules have energy which they can use to "fix" carbon dioxide (CO_2), that is to link CO_2 molecules together with the addition of hydrogens to form glucose molecules. This process takes many steps.

Both photolysis and CO_2 fixation take place within chloroplasts. About 75 per cent of the light energy which activates the chlorophyll is trapped as potential chemical energy in the glucose molecule.

SYNTHESIS OF OTHER MOLECULES IN ANIMALS AND PLANTS —

1) Carbohydrates — Sugars are soluble in water and are relatively reactive molecules. Because they are soluble they also play a role in osmosis. Plants store carbohydrates as starch in special leucoplasts and they use cellulose (another polymer of glucose units) as a structural material.

Animals store carbohydrates as glycogen, another glucose polymer. Glycogen is stored primarily in liver and muscle cells. If an excess of sugar is available to living organisms it is often converted to, and stored as, fat or oil.

2) Fats (lipids) — Lipid is a general term given to organic molecules that are soluble in "fat solvents" such as ether. The group includes fats, oils, waxes and phospholipids. In most plants and animals lipids constitute the largest source of stored energy. Phospholipids which are special fatty acid molecules with a phosphate (PO_4) group attached, form an important structural part of cell membranes. In general, the intermediate (2 and 3 carbon) molecules of carbohydrate or lipid metabolism are interchangeable and can be built up to form either carbohydrates or lipids.

3) Amino Acids and Proteins — Plant cells and animal cells differ greatly in their ability to synthesize amino acids. Plant cells can make all 22 and can synthesize the amino group, NH_2, from ammonium NH_4^+, nitrate NO_3^- or nitrite NO_2^- ions found in the soil. Nitrogen-fixing bacteria associated with leguminous plants such as peas, beans and clover, can change atmospheric molecular nitrogen, N_2, into ammonia NH_3, which the plant can then convert into NH_2. All animal cells depend on plant cells to make NH_2 for them, and most animal cells lack the ability to make the carbon chains of 8 or 10 of the amino acids. Any amino acid which an animal cell cannot make is considered "essential" since it must be supplied in the diet. Both plant and animal cells can shift the amino group from one amino acid to another carbon chain. This process is known as transamination.

Protein molecules consist of chains of amino acids from 50 to 2000 units long. The amino acids are arranged with great precision and if even one amino acid is missing or out of sequence the protein will not function properly as an enzyme or as a structural unit of the cell. Consider the difference in meaning between the two words heat and hate. Only the sequence of the letters has been changed and yet these words function in completely different ways. Similarly changing the sequence of amino acids in protein molecules can change the way the protein can function. Protein synthesis is controlled by the genetic material DNA found in the cell nucleus. The details of this are described later in these notes.

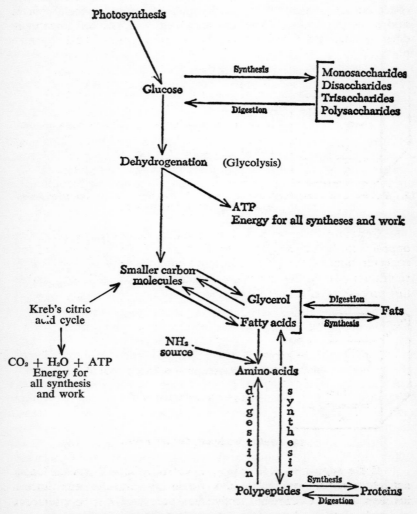

14. Pathways of metabolism. Note that fat and protein molecules can be used in cellular respiration.

FUNCTIONS OF CELL MEMBRANES

(For structure see section on cell structure.) Cell membranes control the traffic of material in and out of the cell. Certain small molecules e.g. CO_2, NH_3 can move through cell membranes by diffusion. There is a net gain in movement of the substance in question from an area of high concentration of that substance to areas of lower concentration of that substance. In such cases the cell membrane is said to be permeable to the substance and since the cell membrane does no work during the process this is an example of passive transport.

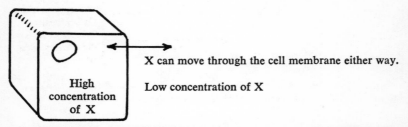

X can move through the cell membrane either way.

High concentration of X

Low concentration of X

15. Passive transport, diagrammatic, more X leaks out of the cell than leaks into it. The cell membrane does no work.

Certain cells have the ability to move substances in a direction opposite to the concentration gradient, that is, from an area of low concentration of the given substance into an area of higher concentration. To do this the cell membrane must expend energy and so this process is called active transport.

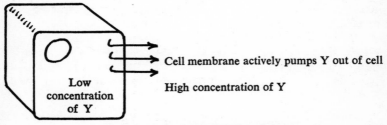

Cell membrane actively pumps Y out of cell

Low concentration of Y

High concentration of Y

16. Active transport, diagrammatic.

If the supply of ATP energy is cut off, the cell can no longer actively transport materials and Y would flow into the cell. Since it involves the use of enzymes, active transport in cells is very selective and only certain substances can be actively transported.

Since cell membranes keep certain molecules in the cell, e.g. proteins, and allow other molecules, e.g. water to move through the membrane, cell membranes are said to be semi-permeable. Under these conditions osmosis can occur. Osmosis is the diffusion of a solvent (water) through a semi-permeable membrane (the cell membrane) from an area of high concentration of the solvent into an area of lower concentration of the solvent.

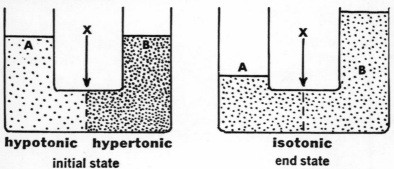

hypotonic   hypertonic   **isotonic**

initial state   **end state**

17. Osmosis. In the initial state, because A is less concentrated than B, water will be pulled from A into B. This eventually leads to the isotonic end state, where concentrations in A and B are equal. From this point on, no further net migration of water occurs (than is, just as much water moves from A into B as from B into A). A semipermeable membrane is represented by X.

IMPORTANCE OF CELL ENVIRONMENT —

The physical conditions surrounding a cell are very important to the cell. There are definite limits of tolerance to changes in the medium in which cells can exist, e.g. red blood cells normally exist surrounded by the liquid part of the blood which is about 94 per cent water. If red blood cells are placed in a concentration of 100 per cent water they will swell up because water is entering the cells by osmosis. This swelling will cause an increased pressure known as turgor pressure on the cell membrane and the membrane will eventually burst.

If red blood cells are placed in a medium that contains much less than 94 per cent water, water will move by osmosis out of the red blood cell causing it to shrink. This reduction in the volume of the protoplasm is known as plasmolysis.

If water is removed from plant cells by evaporation or other means, the turgor pressure in the plant cells drops; this causes the leaves and other structures to droop and the plant is said to be wilting.

EXPERIMENT TO SHOW OSMOSIS —

Method — if parchment cup is not available for the semi-permeable membrane, use inner membrane of a fresh egg. Seal glass tube to end of egg with a good sealing wax; pierce shell and membrane under end of tube; remove part of outer shell at opposite end of egg by leaving in dilute hydrochloric acid — thus exposing thin egg membrane; suspend egg in beaker of water with exposed membrane submerged; leave for some time and observe.

Observations: —

1) Liquid (egg contents + water) has risen up tube; stops rising after some hours.

2) Water in beaker is still clear.

Conclusions: —

1) Water has entered egg through membrane.

2) Membrane has prevented dissolved substances in egg from going out into water.

3) Egg membrane is therefore semi-permeable.

4) The process of w a t e r movement through the membrane is osmosis — direction is toward a lower concentration of water.

5) Finally the w e i g h t of liquid in the tube produces a pres-. sure on the inside of the membrane which prevents water from going in — this pressure is equal to the osmotic pressure of the egg contents (solution).

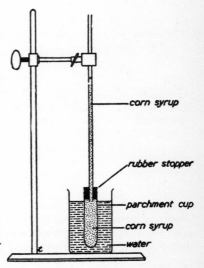

corn syrup

rubber stopper

parchment cup

corn syrup

water

18. **Apparatus to demonstrate osmosis.**

EXPERIMENT TO SHOW PLASMOLYSIS —

Method — Place some *spirogyra* filaments on slide in 10% sugar or salt solution, cover with cover glass and observe under microscope; to reverse process remove solution by blotter and replace with water.

42

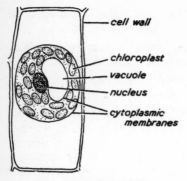

19. **Plasmolysed cell.**

Observations: —

1) Plasma membrane shrinks from cell wall.

2) Vacuole shrinks.

3) Cell contents return to normal when solution is replaced by water.

Conclusions: —

1) Water leaves the cell since there is a lower concentration of water outside than inside — by osmosis outwards.

2) The cell is said to be plasmolyzed.

3) When the plasmolyzed cell is placed in water again some water goes back into the cell by osmosis.

4) Cells will die if plasmolyzed for long periods.

Turgor and Wilting — The turgor pressure is the outward pressure on the cell wall brought about by the intake of water by osmosis — this is 50 lbs. per sq. inch or more. It is this pressure which causes the rigidity of leaves and other soft plant parts. Loss of turgor pressure by excessive transpiration or too dry soil causes wilting. Wilted cells, if alive will draw in water — e.g. crisping of lettuce in cold water.

MITOSIS —

This is the most common type of cell division. During mitosis there is a precise doubling of the chromosomes and an equal distribution, both qualitatively and quantitatively, of the chromosomes to the daughter cells.

Mitosis is a continuous process but for descriptive purposes can be broken into a number of steps:

1) Interphase — chromatin material (DNA) that will form the chromosomes duplicates itself exactly.

2) Prophase — chromatin material in the nucleus forms chromosomes which appear as long, thin threads which gradually shorten and thicken. Individual chromosomes are double structures consisting of 2 chromatids held together at one point by a centromere. Centrioles, found chiefly in animal cells, divide and migrate to opposite ends of the nucleus; the nucleolus and nuclear membrane disappear; the spindle forms.

3) **Metaphase** — the chromosomes line up arranged in a single line, the spindle fibres attach themselves to the centromeres.

4) **Anaphase** — each centromere splits and the chromatids of each chromosome separate and migrate to the poles of the spindle; each chromatid is now a daughter chromosome.

5) **Telophase** — a nucleus forms at each pole; the chromosomes change back into diffuse chromatin material; nuclear membrane reappears. In animal cells the spindle fibres disappear and a constriction across the cytoplasm forms and separates the cells. In plant cells a cell plate which forms a cell wall develops and divides the cytoplasm.

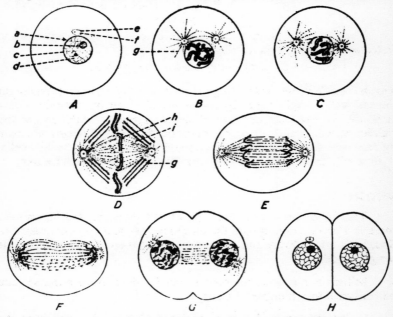

20. **Mitosis in an animal cell, diagrammatic. A, interphase cell. B, early prophase. C, late prophase. D, metaphase. E, anaphase. F, early telophase. G, late telophase. H, daughter cells. a, nucleus. b, nucleolus. c, nuclear membrane. d, chomatin. e, centrosphere. f, centriole. g, astral ray. h, chromosome. i, spindle.**

Chromosomes — consist of long double strands of deoxyribonucleic acid, DNA, surrounded by a protein envelope. (See section on the

44

structure of nucleic acids.) The DNA molecules can be thought of as the structures in the cell that carry the plans of the cell. The plans are written in a code and the code is formed by the linear arrangement of the purine and pyrimidine molecules in the DNA strands. Figure 21 shows a short section of double-stranded DNA. The differences in the size of the molecules between purines and pyrimidines and their atomic arrangement is such that only adenine will link with thymine and only guanine will link with cytosine. The sugar and phosophate molecules serve as a backbone and do not affect the coding.

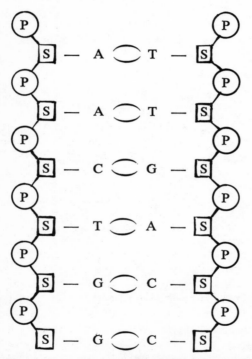

21.   Short section of double stranded DNA, diagrammatic

(P) = phosphate

[S] = sugar (desoxy ribose)

A = adenine   } purines
G = guanine   }

C = cytosine } pyrimidines
T = thymine   }

⌣ = hydrogen bond

Chromosomes can be thought of as double-strand DNA molecules hundreds of thousands of units long. When chromosomes duplicate themselves during interphase they do it by splitting the double strand of DNA and having each single strand used as a template to form another complimentary strand of DNA.

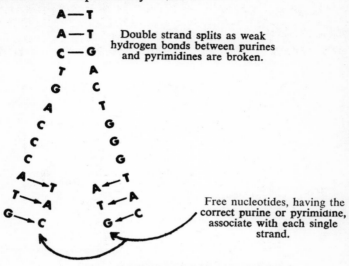

22. **Duplication of DNA, diagrammatic**

DNA can also cause the formation of specific pieces of the other nucleic acid, ribonucleic acid, RNA. Instead of deoxyribose, the 5-carbon sugar in the RNA chain is ribose and instead of the pyrimidine thymine lining up with the purine adenine, another pyrimidine, uracil is used. Thus DNA with the code — A A C G T T G C would cause the formation of RNA with
the complimentary code —   U U G C A A C G
Actually DNA makes 2 kinds of RNA:

1) **Messenger RNA** — relatively long chains of single strand RNA (hundreds of nucleotide units).

2) **Transfer RNA** — relatively short chains of RNA (30 to 50 nucleotide units).

PROTEIN SYNTHESIS IN CELLS —

The above 2 types of RNA are used to make the specific polypeptide or protein molecules that are used in cells. (See Figure 23 and 24.)

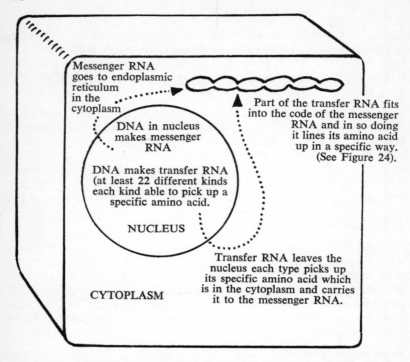

Messenger RNA goes to endoplasmic reticulum in the cytoplasm

Part of the transfer RNA fits into the code of the messenger RNA and in so doing it lines its amino acid up in a specific way. (See Figure 24).

DNA in nucleus makes messenger RNA

DNA makes transfer RNA (at least 22 different kinds each kind able to pick up a specific amino acid.

NUCLEUS

Transfer RNA leaves the nucleus each type picks up its specific amino acid which is in the cytoplasm and carries it to the messenger RNA.

CYTOPLASM

23. **The way DNA, RNA and amino acids react to form a specific protein in a cell, diagrammatic.**

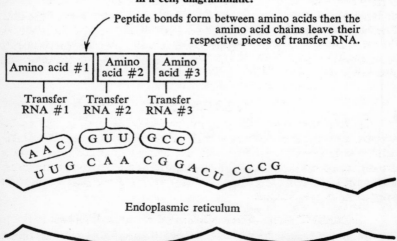

Peptide bonds form between amino acids then the amino acid chains leave their respective pieces of transfer RNA.

Amino acid #1 | Amino acid #2 | Amino acid #3

Transfer RNA #1 | Transfer RNA #2 | Transfer RNA #3

A A C | G U U | G C C

U U G C A A C G G A C U C C C G

Endoplasmic reticulum

24. **The way messenger RNA, transfer RNA and amino acids may fit together, diagrammatic.**

Genes — A gene is enough DNA code on a chromosome to provide the information to cause the formation of a protein molecule.

REGULATION OF METABOLISM, GROWTH AND DEVELOPMENT OF CELLS —

With the exception of the reproductive cells, sperm and eggs, each cell in a multi-celled organism contains the same DNA-encoded genetic information. That means that liver cells have the code to make all the proteins found in the kidney cells or nerve cells. Similarly in plants, leaf cells have the information to make the colours found in flower petals yet they do not. Obviously there must be something regulating the kinds of DNA code that are used by specific cells and consequently these cells make only specific proteins which act as enzymes and regulate the cell's chemistry.

All of the processes which are responsible for this regulation are not known, but the regulation is caused by specific cells trading molecules with other cells. These messenger molecules turn on and turn off specific parts of the DNA code. Since the DNA makes the RNA that makes the enzymes that do all of the chemical work in cells, regulation of the DNA is sufficient to regulate the development, growth and metabolism of cells.

Mechanism of Virus Action — Viruses consist of strands of DNA or RNA sheathed in protein. The virus has the ability to attach itself to certain cells and inject its DNA or RNA into the cell. The virus DNA or RNA then takes over the control of the chemistry of the host cell. The host DNA is shut off and the host cell is directed by the code on the virus DNA or RNA to manufacture more virus. After a relatively short time the host cell dies and breaks open, releasing thousands of new virus particles.

ORGANISMS

In this unit two complex, multicellular organisms are to be studied, a mammal and a herbaceous, dicotyledenous plant. All multicellular organisms have cells which are organized into tissues; tissues are organized into interacting systems called organs, organs form interacting organ systems and the organism consists of the sum of all of its interacting organ systems.

DISSECTION AND STUDY OF A MAMMAL

Man is a mammal and, with the exception of his upright posture and exceptionally highly developed brain, he is quite characteristic of this class of animal. Although you will not be dissecting a human, the structures of your experimental animal will differ very little from those of man and since most students are interested in how their own bodies function, human examples have been used in this section.

ORGANIZATION OF THE MAMMALIAN BODY —

(a) **Cells** — Billions of microscopic cells are produced by mitotic cell division from the zygote.

(b) **Tissues** — A tissue is a group of cells similar in structure and doing the same work.

KINDS OF TISSUES:

1) **Epithelial** — covering, lining, secretion; may be simple (one layer) or stratified (several layers).

e.g. squamous — flat plates inside mouth.

columnar — long narrow cells, inside alimentary canal, ciliated type in windpipe.

goblet — mucous cells in gullet secrete mucus.

2) **Connective** — many forms, strength, joining, storage, etc.

adipose — fat, large cells in deep skin, contain fat globules — storage.

yellow fibrous — branched yellow elastic fibres — external ears, vocal cords.

white fibrous — non-elastic tendons — join muscles to bones.

cartilage — living cells in non-cellular mass — nose, windpipe, cushions between bones at joints.

bone — a few living cells in non-cellular mass; much calcium phosphate deposited to harden; has blood vessels and nerves so is a living tissue.

3) **Muscle** — long cells (fibres) which can contract and relax.

striated voluntary — striated fibres with several nuclei, arranged in bundles; voluntary movements — e.g. biceps.

smooth involuntary — smooth fibres, one nucleus; wall of digestive tract — involuntary movement.

cardiac — network of striated branched fibres; found only in heart — pump blood; involuntary.

4) **Nerve** — neurons (cell body, axon, dendrite); any nerve, brain, spinal cord; carry impulses for co-ordination of body parts.

5) **Circulatory** — fluid tissues, blood and lymph; transportation of food, oxygen, etc.

6) Reproductive — sperms and eggs — reproduction.

(c) Organs — Several tissues working together to do a certain job — e.g. heart contains epithelial, muscle, circulatory and nerve tissues working together to pump blood.

(d) Systems — A group of organs doing related work — e.g. digestive system contains mouth, gullet, stomach, intestine, liver, pancreas; these organs all do work concerned with obtaining, digesting, and absorbing food materials.

STRUCTURE AND FUNCTION OF ORGAN SYSTEMS —

DIGESTIVE SYSTEM —
(See section on digestion previously included).

CIRCULATORY SYSTEM —

BLOOD COMPOSITION —
1) Plasma — a straw coloured liquid containing 90% water and various dissolved constituents as follows:

Blood proteins — fibrinogen etc. (see use later).

Nutritive — glucose, amino acids, fats.

Wastes — carbon dioxide, urea.

Inorganic salts — sodium chloride, sodium bicarbonate, phosphates, potassium and calcium compounds etc.

2) Solids — cells make up 40-50% of the blood.

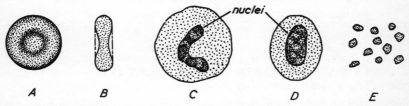

25.   Types of blood cells. A, red cell (erythrocyte), surface view. B, same red cell, in section. C, leucocyte. D, lymphocyte. E, blood platelets.

Red Cells — (erythrocytes) discs concave on sides, 1/3000 inch in diameter, no nuclei, contain haemoglobin, 5 million per cubic millimetre, made in red marrow of vertebrae, ribs, arms and legs, live 10 to 30 days, destroyed in liver and spleen when worn out, iron from haemoglobin stored in liver, rest of haemoglobin excreted as bile pigment, use — to transport oxygen.

50

White Cells — larger and fewer than red (1 white to 600 red) 2 kinds:
  i. **Leucocytes** — (phagocytes) made in bone marrow; lobed nucleus, can pass from capillaries into tissues with lymph, defend against bacteria, help remove dead tissue.
  ii. **Lymphocytes** — made in spleen and lymph glands; nuclei not lobed, may turn into scar tissue.

Platelets — small discs, number between red and white, made in bone marrow and in lungs; assist in blood clotting (see later).

USES OF BLOOD SYSTEM —
1) Carry food from digestive organs to tissue cells.

2) Carry oxygen from lungs to cells and carbon dioxide from cells to lungs.

3) Carry urea from liver to kidneys for excretion.

4) Carry hormones from endocrine glands to organs which they control.

5) Fight disease by antibodies and white cells.

6) Regulate body temperature by carrying heat to skin for radiation and providing water for perspiration.

7) Carry necessary water to tissue cells.

HEART STRUCTURE AND ACTION —
A muscular organ consisting of an auricle and a ventricle on each side — actually 2 pumps working together. Separating auricles from ventricles are valves — tough membranes held by tendons when closed by pressure in ventricles. Heart is surrounded by a double sac (pericardium) to prevent friction with lungs. Heart in centre of chest cavity.

CARDIAC CYCLE IS SERIES OF ACTIONS IN ONE BEAT —
1) Two auricles fill with blood (oxygenated into left from pulmonary veins and deoxygenated into right from caval veins).

2) Auricles contract together, pressure opens bicuspid and tricuspid valves and forces blood into ventricles.

3) Ventricles contract together — pressure closing valves (above) and opening semilunar valves into aorta and pulmonary artery.

4) Blood forced into arteries, ventricles then relax and pressure in arteries closes semilunar valves to prevent blood from flowing back into ventricles.

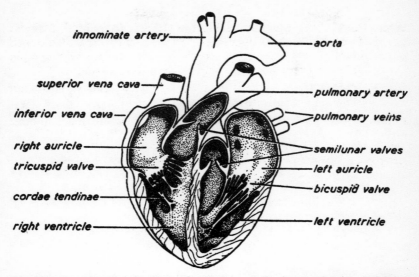

innominate artery — aorta
superior vena cava — pulmonary artery
inferior vena cava — pulmonary veins
right auricle — semilunar valves
tricuspid valve — left auricle
cordae tendinae — bicuspid valve
right ventricle — left ventricle

26. Diagram showing the internal structure of the human heart. Adjoining blood vessels are also included. The term "atrium", in place of "auricle" to designate the receiving chambers of the heart, is considered more correct but is not so commonly used.

Systole — contraction of ventricles.

Diastole — relaxation (expansion) of ventricles.

BLOOD VESSEL STRUCTURE —

1) Arteries — carry blood away from heart, largest is one inch diameter (aorta); three layers in walls — outer tough, middle thick, elastic muscle and inner smooth, single layer of cells; contraction of expanded arteries maintains blood pressure when ventricles relax.

Pulse is wave of blood through arteries when ventricles contract — can only be felt where artery is close to surface, for example, radial artery in wrist.

2) Arterioles — branches of arteries — 1/12 inch in diameter, thinner muscular wall; nerves control size of arteries and arterioles to control blood supply to different organs.

3) Capillaries — about the diameter of a red cell (1/3000 inch); one layer of cells in wall; large total cross section makes blood move slowly — diffusion possible.

4) Veins — collect blood from capillaries; same three layers in walls as in arteries but very thin muscle layer; cup-shaped valves in large veins prevent back flow of blood — especially in lower body; no pulse; carry blood toward heart — all deoxygenated except pulmonary vein.

BLOOD PRESSURE —

Provided by contraction of ventricles. Difference in pressure causes blood to flow from ventricles through arteries, and capillaries and veins back to auricles — the drop in pressure being from 120 millimetres to 5 millimetres. Most of the drop is due to large total cross sectional area of capillaries. Systolic pressure is peak pressure in arteries when ventricles contract — (approx. 120 millimetres). Diastolic pressure is pressure in arteries when ventricles relax — (approx. 80 millimetres). Pressure stays up to 80 millimetres at relaxation for several reasons:

    i. Elasticity of arterial walls.

    ii. Resistance of capillary walls.

    iii. Viscosity of blood.

BLOOD CIRCULATION —

The mammal has complete double circulation (i.e. the blood visits the heart twice during each complete circuit — oxygenated and deoxygenated, and the two kinds of blood are kept completely separated in the heart).

1) **Pulmonary circulation** — deoxygenated blood from the right ventricle through the pulmonary artery to the lung capillaries for exchange of oxygen and carbon dioxide; oxygenated blood then returns by 4 pulmonary veins to the left auricle; requires 11 seconds; purpose — oxygenation of the blood.

2) **Systemic circulation** — oxygenated blood from the left ventricle through the aorta which arches up over the heart and descends on the dorsal side; aorta gives off branches to all body parts except the lungs (carotid to head, subclavian to arms, hepatic to liver, gastric to stomach, mesenteric to intestine, renals to kidneys, genitals to reproductive system, iliacs to legs); after branching to capillaries in tissues and doing its work the blood returns by inferior and superior vena-cava to the right auricle; purpose — to carry food and oxygen to the tissue cells and to collect wastes; requires about 30 heart beats to send blood to lower part of body and back to heart.

3) **Hepatic Portal Circulation** — part of systemic blood from intestinal wall through the hepatic portal vein to the liver; purpose —

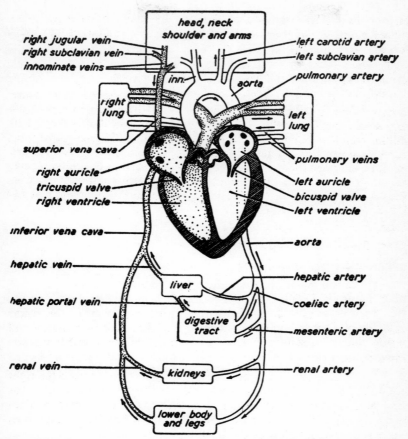

right jugular vein
right subclavian vein
innominate veins

head, neck
shoulder and arms

left carotid artery
left subclavian artery
pulmonary artery

inn.

aorta

right lung

left lung

superior vena cava

pulmonary veins

right auricle
tricuspid valve
right ventricle

left auricle
bicuspid valve
left ventricle

inferior vena cava

aorta

hepatic vein

hepatic artery

liver

hepatic portal vein

coeliac artery

digestive tract

mesenteric artery

renal vein

kidneys

renal artery

lower body and legs

27. Diagrammatic representation of the pulmonary and systemic circulation of the human; inn, innominate artery.

temporary storage of part of the absorbed food as glycogen in liver cells; blood leaves liver by hepatic vein to inferior vena-cava to right auricle.

4) **Coronary circulation** — two coronary arteries are the first branches from the aorta; they divide to form capillaries in the heart muscle; purpose — to supply the heart muscle with food and oxygen and to collect waste from its cells; blood then returns to the coronary sinus which empties it into the right auricle; only two seconds required.

LYMPH CIRCULATION —

Lymph is blood plasma containing food and oxygen and some white cells; it goes out through walls of capillaries and bathes the tissue cells to carry food and oxygen to them and remove wastes; lymph vessels collect the lymph and conduct it up to the large thoracic lymph duct in the left chest where it joins the left subclavian vein — thus putting the lymph back into the blood; lymph nodes are swellings on lymph vessels where there are numerous capillaries and many white cells; lymph is kept moving by muscular action, breathing, etc.; uses of lymph are:

1) Carries food and oxygen to cells and wastes back to the blood.

2) Carries fats from villi to blood.

3) Filters out bacteria in lymph nodes.

4) Produces lymphocytes.

SPECIAL BLOOD FUNCTIONS —

1) Clotting — to prevent blood loss and heal wounds. Platelets, fibrinogen and calcium ions necessary; clotting usually caused by injury to wall of blood vessel; platelets injured by rubbing on rough wall liberate thromboplastin which starts a chain of reactions; result is the change of soluble fibrinogen to insoluble fibrin which precipitates forming threads which entangle corpuscles and platelets forming a clot.

Haemophilia — slow clotting or refusal to clot.

2) Temperature Control

To raise temperature:
i. Metabolic rate increases.
ii. Blood vessels close to skin contract to diminish radiation.

To lower temperature:
i. Blood carries heat from interior to skin for radiation.
ii. Blood supplies water for perspiration which cools body by evaporation.
Perspiration is water + 1% solids — mostly sodium chloride.
iii. Evaporation of water into lung air uses heat.
iv. Decrease metabolic rate.

3) Resistance to Disease

White cells carried by blood to where they are needed to kill bacteria. Blood produces antibodies to counteract toxins produced by bacteria.

USES OF SPLEEN —

1) Contains a reserve supply of blood for emergencies — as much as 1/6 of blood in body.

2) Produces lymphocytes.

3) Destroys worn out red blood cells.

RESPIRATORY SYSTEM —

Breathing (external respiration) — the mechanical process of inspiring oxygen and expiring the carbon dioxide produced.

1) Structure of System

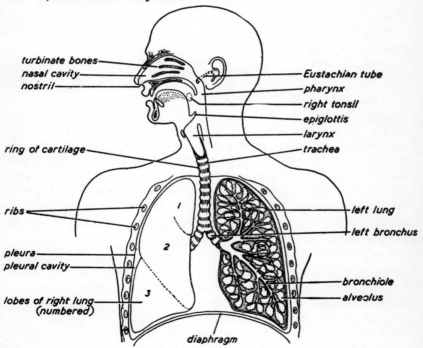

turbinate bones
nasal cavity
nostril

Eustachian tube
pharynx
right tonsil
epiglottis
larynx
trachea

ring of cartilage

ribs

left lung
left bronchus

pleura
pleural cavity

bronchiole
alveolus

lobes of right lung
(numbered)

diaphragm

28. The human respiratory system.

nostrils — external openings.

nasal cavities — in front central section of skull; lined by moist, ciliated, mucous membranes.

turbinate bones — partially divide nasal cavities.

sinuses — cavities in face bones opening from nasal cavities.

nasal openings — 2 from nasal cavities into pharynx. Up to this point the air has been filtered by hairs and cilia and warmed and moistened by mucous membranes.

glottis — opening from pharynx to trachea; glottis covered by epiglottis during swallowing.

larynx — voice box at top of trachea; has 2 vocal cords for sound production.

trachea — one inch in diameter; muscle and elastic tissue; c shaped cartilage rings for support; capable of some expansion and contraction to control intake of air; ciliated mucous membrane catches dust.

bronchi — two branches of trachea which in turn branch into five bronchial tubes to five lung lobes.

lungs — right 3 lobes, left 2 lobes; bronchial tubes branch to smaller bronchioles which end in air sacs surrounded by smaller air sacs called alveoli; alveoli have thin walls (one cell thick and are surrounded by thin walled blood capilaries; very large total surface area; moist surface for diffusion; lungs are on each side of heart in thoracic cavity; each lung in a sac of two layers (pleura) to prevent friction with wall of chest.

2) Breathing Action

Inspiration — muscles between ribs lift ribs up and forward; diaphragm, arched up when relaxed, contracts and flattens; these two processes increase volume of thoracic cavity and reduce pressure in lungs. Greater pressure outside forces air into elastic lungs.

Expiration — inspiration muscles relax and weight of chest returns it to its previous size forcing out air. Forced expiration by muscular action may expel more air.

EXCHANGE OF GASES —

Blood brought to lungs from tissues contains a low concentration of oxygen and a high concentration of carbon dioxide compared with air in alveoli; oxygen diffuses into blood from air and carbon dioxide diffuses from blood into air.

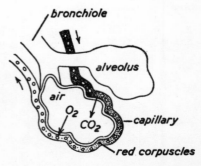

Inspired air oxygen 20%, carbon dioxide 0.04%.

Expired a i r oxygen 16%, carbon dioxide 4.4%.

29. Diagram to show exchange of gases between alveoli and capillaries.

TRANSPORTATION OF GASES AND RESPIRATION IN CELLS —

Oxygen combines with dark red haemoglobin of red blood cells forming bright red oxy-haemoglobin; this is carried to capillaries in tissues where oxygen is released and diffuses out of capillaries through lymph to tissue cells. In cells food is oxidized to release energy needed — this process is respiration proper. Carbon dioxide produced diffuses back into capillaries and is carried by the blood partly dissolved in plasma and partly combined in sodium and potassium bicarbonates.

REGULATION OF BREATHING RATE —

Breathing rate controlled by nerves from medulla of brain to breathing muscles. Increase in carbon dioxide content of blood affects nervous system to increase rate. Fear or excitement may increase rate. Very low percentage of oxygen in air may increase rate.

ELIMINATION SYSTEMS —

Excretion is the removal, from the living protoplasm of the waste products of metabolism, e.g. CO_2, H_2O, nitrogenous wastes and salt.

1) The Lungs — eliminate CO_2 and H_2O.

2) Alimentary Canal — eliminates bile pigment (waste part of haemoglobin) and egests (but does not excrete) undigested food.

3) Skin — outer epidermis of many cell layers produces hair, nails, etc.; inner dermis is thicker, connective tissue which contains blood and lymph vessels, sweat glands, nerves, oil glands, etc.; skin excretes water with 1% dissolved solids (mostly salt) from perspiration glands.

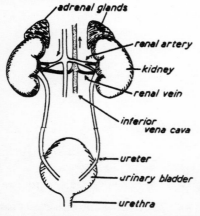

30. **Posterior view of the human urinary system and the adrenal glands.**

4) Kidneys — two reddish-brown organs 2 inches x 4 inches at sides of vertebral column in lower back; three tubes attached near centre — renal artery, renal vein and ureter; outer cortex and inner medulla consist of numerous nephrons (filtering units); each nephron has a filtering capsule (Bowman's capsule) enclosing a capillary mass from the renal artery; to the capsule is attached a tubule which leads to the renal pelvis (enlarged end of ureter).

Filtering Action — from blood is capillary into Bowman's capsule diffuse waster, urea, glucose, mineral salts; this solution proceeds down the tubule.

Reabsorption — nearly all the useful material — glucose, minerals and some water — is reabsorbed from the tubule into a blood capillary surrounding it; the waste material (urea) dissolved in water passes down the tubule to the renal pelvis, then through the ureter to the urinary bladder — as urine. Urea (nitrogenous waste) is produced in the body by tearing down worn out cells and when excess protein is oxidized for energy (explained previously).

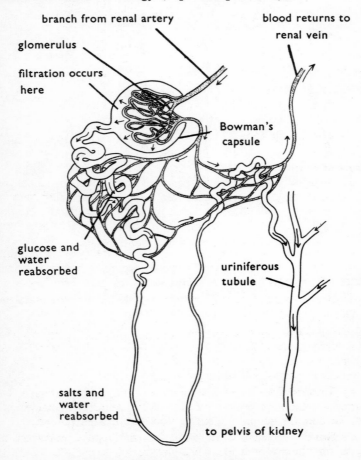

31.   Diagram of glomerulus and Bowman's capsule.

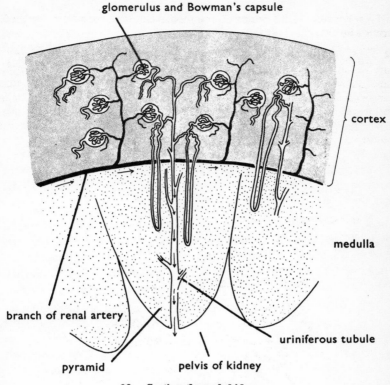

32. Section through kidney.

MUSCULAR AND SKELETAL SYSTEMS —

These two systems work together to provide movement, support and, in the case of the skull, protection.

Skeletal System — The skeleton of man is fairly typical. It consists of two parts, the axial skeleton consisting of the skull, vertebral column and ribs, and the apendicular skeleton which includes the arms and legs and their points of attachment, the pelvic and pectoral girdles.

1) Vertebral Column — divided into the neck (cervical), chest (thoracic), black (lumbar), pelvic (sacral), and tail (caudal) portions. In man the caudal bones are fused to form the coccyx.

2) Skull — consists of flat bones which are fused together. It is made up of the cranium, the sense capsules and portions of the visceral arches (jaws).

3) Girdles — the limbs are attached to and supported by two rings of bones called girdles — the pelvic (hip) girdle and the pectoral (shoulder) girdle. The pelvic girdle in man is modified for upright posture and consists of the fusion of paired ilia, ischia and pubic bones. The pectoral girdle is composed of the scapulas (shoulder blades) and the clavicles (collar bones).

4) Limbs — the arms are composed of a humerus which is attached to the shoulder girdle, the radius and ulna (forearm bones), the carpals (wrist bones, metacarpals (hand bones) and digits (finger bones). The leg bones are the femur, attached to the hip; a tibia and fibula (foreleg bones), tarsals (ankle bones), metatarsals (foot bones) and digits (toe bones). Each leg also contains a patella (knee cap) and calcar (heel).

Muscular System — There are three types of muscle cells — skeletal (striated), visceral (smooth), and cardiac (heart). All muscle cells work the same way, by contraction. The effect of these contractions depend on where the muscles are located and where they are attached in the body.

1) Skeletal Muscle — also known as striated or voluntary muscle. These muscle cells are cylindrical in cross section and have many nuclei which are located close under the cell membrane or sarcolemma. The cells are arranged in bundles and the bundles joined together to form motor units. Muscle fibres are surrounded by connective tissue, which forms tendons at the ends of the muscles and attaches the muscles to the bones or to other muscles. Muscles are arranged in antagonistic pairs — as one contracts its antagonist is stretched.

2) Visceral Muscle — also known as smooth and involuntary muscle. These muscle cells are spindle-shaped and have only one nucleus. The cells are arranged in layers, usually two layers at right angles to one another, e.g. the circular and longitudinal muscles of the stomach wall. Contraction of these muscle layers results in lengthening or shortening of hollow organs, e.g. peristalsis in the intestine.

3) Cardiac Muscle — also known as heart muscle. Special striated, involuntary muscle, each cell having only one nucleus.

Muscle cell contraction uses up energy. This energy is supplied by ATP and is replaced by cellular respiration.

REPRODUCTIVE SYSTEMS —

Man is viviparous; the female sex cells, the eggs, are retained within the female. Fertilization is internal, the young develop within the female and are born in a fairly advanced state of development.

1) Male Systems — The external genitalia of the human male consists of the testes, scrotum and penis. The testes produce the sperm and the male sex hormone, testosterone. The sperm is transferred to paired seminal vesicles where it is temporarily stored. From the seminal vesicles the sperm moves in a tube, the vas deferens, to the urethra. The prostate gland surrounds the point where the vas deferens joins the urethra. At the base of the penis are two other glands — Cowper's glands. The ejaculatory mass (semen) contains sperm and secretions from the seminal vesicles, prostate gland and Cowper's glands.

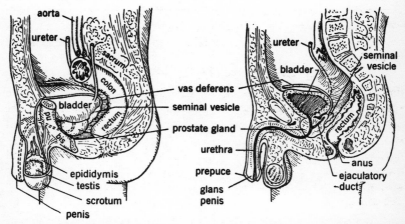

33. The male urogenital system. Left, **in perspective;** Right, **Median section.**

2) Female Systems — The essential parts of the female reproductive system are: the ovaries, which produce the egg cells; the oviducts, which are tubes that carry the egg cells to the uterus; the uterus, where the fertilized egg can become attached.

The external genitalia consist of lip-like folds of tissue, the labium majus and minus, and the clitoris. The labia surround the orifice of the vagina which leads to the uterus.

(See Figure 34 — Next Page)

62

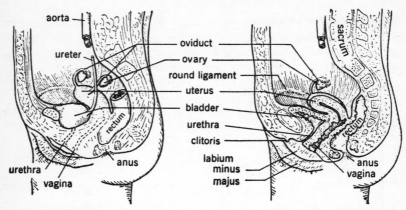

34. **The female urogenital system.** Left, **in perspective;** Right, **Median section.**

CO-ORDINATION AND CONTROL SYSTEMS —

A complex organism must have means of co-ordinating the functioning of the various organs. This consists of nervous regulation by the nervous system and certain sense organs (eye, etc.) and chemical regulation by endocrine glands.

NERVOUS SYSTEM AND SENSE ORGANS —

Unit of structure is the neuron — consisting of a cell body (nucleus, cytoplasm, etc.) with projections or fibres called axon and dendrite. There are 3 kinds of neuron:

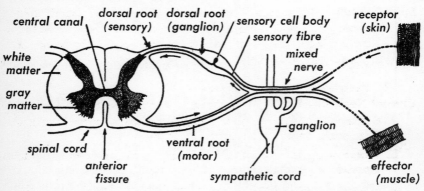

35. **Cross section of the spinal cord of man showing the relationship of the spinal cord to the spinal nerves.**

Sensory — carry impulses from sense organs to central nervous system.

Motor — carry impulses from central nervous system to muscles or glands.

Connector — join other 2 kinds.

Synapse — is the place where impulse passes from axon of one neuron to dendrite of another — no actual contact. Neuron cell bodies are only found in brain cortex, interior of spinal cord or in ganglia.

1) **Central Nervous System** — brain and spinal cord.
Brain — in cranium enclosed by 3 membranes (meninges) with cerebro-spinal fluid between; grey matter (cortex) on outside consists of cell bodies and white matter, inside, consists of fibres (axons and dendrites).

Cerebrum — 9/10 of brain, 2 hemispheres with irregular convulutions, cavity (ventricle) in centre of each; no optic or olfactory lobes; sensory and motor regions. Uses — thought, reason, memory, receives sensations from sense organs, controls voluntary actions.

Cerebellum — below hind part of cerebrum; 2 hemispheres with parallel striations; use — muscular co-ordination and equilibrium control.

Medulla — one inch long, on floor of skull, continuous with spinal cord; use — controls work of vital organs such as heart, lungs, digestive organs — also originates several cranial nerves.

Spinal Cord — soft, white, 18 inches x ½ inch thick; 3 membranes and cerebro-spinal fluid continuous with those surrounding brain; uses — carries impulses to and from brain and acts as the centre of some reflex actions; grey matter inside; has central canal.

2) **Peripheral Nervous System** —
Cranial Nerves — 12 pairs from brain to parts of head — 3 kinds:
  i. **Sensory** — olfactory, optic, auditory, etc. — carry impulses from sense organs to brain.
  ii. **Motor** — e.g. to eye muscles — carry impulses from brain to muscles or glands.
  iii. **Mixed** — contain both sensory and motor fibres — e.g. the facial nerve carries impulses from brain to face muscles and also carries impulses from tongue nerve endings to brain.

Spinal Nerves — 31 pairs, all mixed nerves, from spinal cord through openings between vertebrae to all parts of body; each has 2 roots — a dorsal root of motor fibres and a ventral root of sensory fibres; motor fibres end in muscles or glands, sensory fibres end in sense organs (nerve endings sensitive to pain, pressure, heat, etc.); ventral root has a ganglion containing sensory cell bodies; motor fibres originate in grey matter of spinal cord.

3) Autonomic (Involuntary) Nervous System — controls involuntary muscular action and gland secretion — 2 parts:

i. Sympathetic — 2 long nerve cords with ganglia, on either side of spinal cord, from which nerve fibres go to heart, alimentary canal, etc.

ii. Parasympathetic — consists of nerves from medulla to eyes, blood vessels, digestive organs, kidneys, etc.

Effects of i. and ii. are often antagonistic — e.g. heart is speeded up by i. and slowed down by ii.

4) Reflex Arc — A reflex is an automatic involuntary act caused by the stimulation of certain nerves. An example is a finger removed automatically from a hot object. The reflex arc here consists of a sensory (receptor) neuron with ending in the skin, a connector neuron and a motor neuron with ending in muscle which removes finger. The sensation does not reach the brain until after the response has been completed.

SPECIAL SENSE ORGANS —
The Eye

1) Protection — bony socket, fat cushion behind eye, eyelids, eyelashes, tear fluid from tear glands above eyes — this washes and moistens eyeball and conjunctiva and drains away into nose through inner corners.

2) Movement — muscles from back of socket to sclerotic coat of eyeball.

i. Rectus muscles — 4 — external, internal, superior and inferior — contraction of muscle moves eyeball in corresponding direction.

ii. Oblique muscles — 2 — superior and inferior — rotate eyeball.

3) Structure — globular, bulged in front, 3 coats:

i. Sclerotic coat — white, tough, front is transparent cornea; shape, protection and muscle attachment; covered in front by thin conjunctiva which lines eyelid.

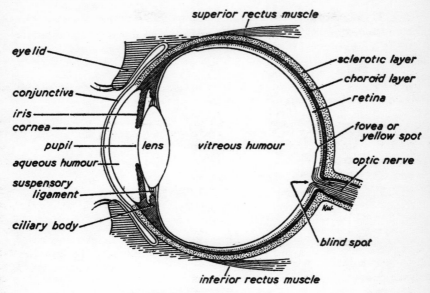

superior rectus muscle

eye lid

conjunctiva

iris

cornea

pupil

lens

vitreous humour

aqueous humour

suspensory ligament

ciliary body

sclerotic layer

choroid layer

retina

fovea or yellow spot

optic nerve

blind spot

inferior rectus muscle

36. The human eye, in section.

ii. Choroid coat — under sclerotic; many blood vessels; pigmented cells prevent internal light reflection; forms coloured iris in front; pupil is opening in iris; size of pupil controlled by sphincter and dilator muscles — size decreases with increased light intensity and with decrease in distance of object.

iii. Retina — inner coat; consists of several layers of nerve cells; light rays forming image, stimulate rods and cones of visual layer which in turn stimulates cells of nervous layer to send messages through optic nerve to the sight area on the cerebrum; rods sensitive to dim light and cones to bright light; blind spot is where optic nerve enters — no rods and cones here; yellow spot is most sensitive area — to see clearly image is focussed on *fovea centralis* at centre of yellow spot.

Lens — bi-convex, elastic, held by ciliary muscles to accommodate for different distances of object — for near object lens must be more bulged.

Humours —
  i. Aqueous — in front of lens — watery liquid.
  ii. Vitreous — behind lens — less fluid.

These give shape to eyeball, support lens, support retina.

Binocular vision — images from 2 eyes go to same area on brain so we have only one image sensation.

4) Defects of Eye:

(a) Presbyopia (old eyes) — lens becomes less elastic and cannot become converging enough for close objects — correct by converging lens for reading, etc.

(b) Myopia (short sighted) — lens too converging forms image in front of retina; correct by diverging lens.

(c) Hypermetropia (long-sighted) — lens not enough converging — image behind retina; correct by converging lens.

(d) Astigmatism — curvature of lens or cornea is different in different diameters; correct by spectacle lens with different curvatures in different directions to compensate.

(e) Cataract — opaque lens for various reasons; in extreme cases lens can be removed and a spectacle lens of similar converging power worn.

The Ear —

1) Structure:

i. Outer ear (pinna) — cartilage and skin; directs sound waves.

ii. Auditory Canal — short tube through skull bone ending in flexible drum or typanic membrane.

iii. Middle ear — a cavity in skull bone traversed by 3 small bones (hammer, anvil, and stirrup) from drum membrane to oval window in inner ear; eustachian tube connects middle ear with pharynx to equalize air pressure on two sides of drum membrane.

iv. Inner ear — two parts with separate functions.

Vestibule — 3 semicircular canals and 2 small sacs, filled with lymph; contains sensory cells with projections into lymph — some projections have limestone crystals attached; movement of head stimulates nerve endings to send messages by vestibular nerve to brain — permits us to be aware of our position; use — to maintain equilibrium.

Cochlea — coiled structure, resembling a snail shell, in bone cavity: lymph filled; membranes divide the coil lengthwise; a row of nerve cells with projecting hairs along one membrane is called the organ of Corti; nerve fibres from the auditory nerve are in contact with these cells.

2) How We Hear:

Sound waves in air enter auditory canal and vibrate drum membrane; vibrations of drum membrane are carried across middle ear by hammer, anvil and stirrup bones to oval window in inner ear; vibrations of oval window are transmitted through lymph to nerve endings of the organ of Corti; these nerve endings are thus stimulated to send impulses through auditory nerve to auditory area on cerebrum where they are interpreted as sound.

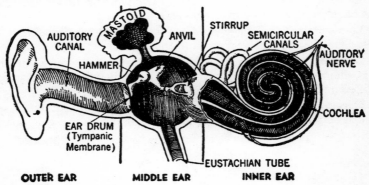

37.   The human ear.

Taste —

Specialized cells located in taste buds in the tongue form junctions with sensory nerve fibres from the brain. These specialized cells can be stimulated by chemicals dissolved in the liquid coating of the

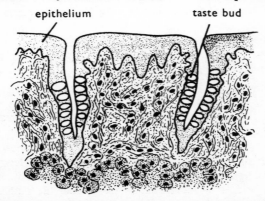

38.   Section through upper surface of tongue to show position of taste buds.

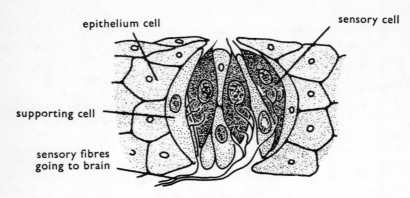

epithelium cell   sensory cell

supporting cell

sensory fibres
going to brain

39. Section through taste bud.

tongue. Four primary tastes can be distinguished — sweet, sour, salty and bitter. Substances which give rise to a sweet taste primarily affect taste buds located at the tip of the tongue, sour and salty sensations are received from taste buds located at the edges of the tongue and bitter substances primarily affect the taste buds at the back of the tongue.

Smell —

Like taste, the sense of smell depends on specialized cells which react to chemicals dissolved in the liquid coating these cells. Chemosensory cells located in the upper part of the nasal cavity are connected by neurons to the brain; these cells are more sensitive than are the taste cells. Four primary odours are detectable: rancid, vinegary, fragrant and burnt.

Temperature —

Scattered throughout the human skin are specialized neural receptors for pressure, pain, heat and cold. Very little is known about

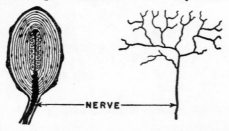

NERVE

40. Two types of sensory structures in man. The structure on the left is found in the deep skin and is sensitive to pressure. The structure on the right is a free nerve ending and is sensitive to pain.

how these receptors function and complex sensations are possible, e.g. ice on the skin may produce a burning sensation by simultaneously stimulating cold, pain and heat receptors.

THE ENDOCRINE SYSTEM —

The endocrine glands of mammals are: the pituitary, thyroid, parathyroid, the islets of Langerhans in the pancreas, adrenals, gonads, parts of the gastric and intestinal wall and, in some mammals, the placenta. These structures are not anatomically related but they all secrete their products into the blood stream and consequently they form an endocrine system. Secretions of the endocrine glands are known as hormones. Hormones have a specific effect on some organ or process.

1) **Pituitary** — 3 lobes (anterior, middle and posterior). A small structure, ½ inch long in man, hanging from the under surface of the brain.

Anterior lobe — produces at least 6 hormones, some of which control other endocrine glands:

(a) thyrotropic hormone (TTH, TSH) — stimulates thyroid to produce and release thyroxin.

(b) follicle-stimulating hormone (FSH) — stimulates growth of ovarian follicles or spermatogenic tubules.

(c) luteinizing hormone (LH) — induces luteinization in developed ovarian follicles, induces ovulation.

(d) lactogenic hormone (LtH) — initiates milk secretion in mammary gland made capable of such secretion by previous action of sex and pituitary hormones.

(e) somatotropin (growth hormone, STH) — stimulates increase in body size; most responsive tissues are skeletal and muscular.

(f) adrenocorticotropic hormone (ACTH) — causes adrenal cortex to produce and release adrenal cortical hormone.

Middle lobe — produces only one hormone:

(a) intermedin (melanocyte-stimulating hormone, MSH) — stimulates dispersion of dark melanin granules in the colour cells of amphibia and fish. Not important in man.

Posterior lobe — produces 2 hormones, both made up of 8 amino acids:

(a) Antidiuretic hormone (vasopressin, ADH) — increases the reabsorbtion of sodium and water from the urine by the distal convoluted tubules of the nephrons of the kidney.

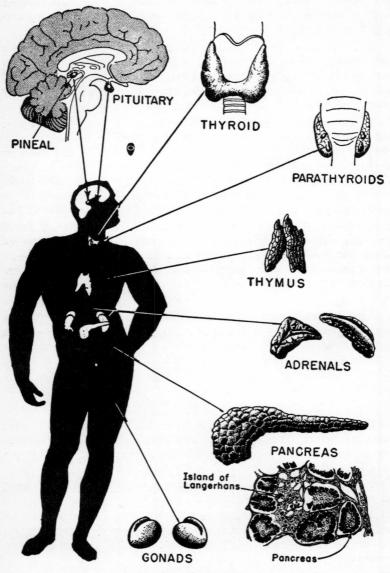

41. The endocrine glands.

(b) Oxytocin — stimulates ejection of milk from the mammary glands after milk production has been initiated, also causes smooth muscles of the uterus to contract.

2) **Thyroid** — has 2 lobes, below and at the sides of the larynx in the throat. Hormone produced is thyroxin, an amino acid that contains iodine. It regulates the basal metabolic rate (B.M.R.). Underactivity can cause goitre, cretinism or myxedema. Overactivity causes high B.M.R., fever, eyes bulge.

3) **Parathyroids** — 2 pairs of small glands located on the ventral surface of the thyroid. Hormone produced is parathormone. It controls calcium metabolism in cells. If hormone level too low, calcium ion is removed from blood and deposited in bones and joints; if hormone level too high, calcium ion withdrawn from bones, blood calcium ion level goes up and much calcium ion is excreted.

4) **Adrenal Cortex** — outside part of adrenal glands; located above kidneys. Produces more than 100 steroids, e.g. cortisone. These have many effects, some influence carbohydrate metabolism by promoting the conversion of glycogen to glucose, others effect kidney tubules promoting the retention of sodium and chloride ions and the excretion of potassium. Other adrenal corticosteroids influence the sex organs.

5) **Adrenal Medulla** — inside part of adrenal glands. Produces adrenalin (epinephrin) and noradrenalin. These hormones working together raise the blood pressure, increase heart rate, promote the conversion of liver glycogen to blood glucose, produce "goose flesh", increase muscular power and resistance to fatigue, promote faster coagulation of the blood and faster responses to external stimuli. These physiological events have been named "the alarm reaction".

6) **Pancreas** — the islets of Langerhans are small groups of cells within this gland. The cells are of two kinds — alpha cells that produce glucagon, and beta cells that produce insulin. The major target organ for both of these hormones is the liver.

(a) glucagon — promotes the breakdown of glycogen in the liver and the enrichment of the blood with glucose.

(b) insulin — removes glucose from the blood by promoting its synthesis into glycogen. If insulin is lacking, blood glucose levels increase from the normal 100 mg. per 100 ml. level. This condition is known as diabetes.

7) **Gonads or Sex Glands** — the testes of the male and the ovaries of the female produce characteristic steriod hormones. An-

drogens such as testosterone contributes to male characteristics, and estrogens such as estradiol contribute to female characteristics. Both types of hormones occur in both sexes; the development of the particular secondary sexual characteristics of males and females depends on the relative balance of these hormones.

8) Ovarian Follicle — after ovulation the luteinizing hormone from the pituitary causes the cells of the ovarian follicle to change into a structure known as the corpus luteum. The corpus luteum releases a hormone, progesterone, which prepares the cells of the uterus for implantation of the egg.

9) Placenta — produces progesterone, helps maintain the developing embryo, prevents miscarriages.

10) Stomach mucosa — produces gastrin, which promotes the release of gastric juice by specialized stomach cells.

11) Intestinal mucosa — produces several hormones known as secretins; they cause liver cells to secrete bile and stimulate the cells of the pancreas to produce and release pancreatic juices.

STEADY STATE CONTROL (HOMEOSTASIS) —

The nervous system and the endocrine system work together to maintain the organism in proper relationship with its environment. The nervous system handles rapid, short term adaptations and the endocrine system slower, longer term controls. The nervous system can act directly on the endocrine system, e.g. stress, such as fear, preceived through the action of the nervous system can cause the release of adrenal cortico hormones that cause the "alarm reaction".

Steady state control mechanisms are highly developed in the mammals, e.g. CO_2 accumulating in the blood stimulates the breathing centre in the brain, which stimulates the muscles associated with breathing to act. If the body is working hard, extra CO_2 is produced; this causes the respiratory centre to signal for increases in both the rate and the depth of breathing which causes extra amounts of CO_2 to be excreted by the lungs. Increases in the rate and depth of breathing also bring increased amounts of O_2 into the body, but the major control of breathing acts through CO_2 concentrations, not O_2 concentrations. Thus increases in CO_2 dissolved in the blood leads to increased breathing which decreases the amount of CO_2 in the blood, CO_2 levels are therefore maintained in a dynamic but steady state.

The control of water balance in animals is very complicated and not completely understood. In terrestrial animals a balance is struck between the amount of water drunk and the amount released by the kidneys for excretion. The thirst centre of the brain and hormones acting on the kidney (ADH, adrenocorticosteroids) are mainly responsible for maintaining this steady state control and also for the control of the concentrations of certain ions in the blood, e.g. Na, Cl, and K.

In all mammals the level of glucose in the blood is held in very strict control. In man the normal level is 100 mg. per 100 ml. of blood. The mechanism of this control is not completely understood but the nervous system and the endocrine system both act.

TABLE 4

CONTROL OF BLOOD GLUCOSE LEVELS

Increases caused by:

(a) ACTH   adrenocorticosteroids   glycogen transformed to glucose
(b) Nervous system   adrenalin   glycogen transformed to glucose
(c) Glucagon   causes liver glycogen to be transformed to glucose

Decreases caused by:

(a) Insulin promotes the transformation of blood glucose to glycogen
(b) Thyroxin   lowers blood glucose by stimulating cellular respiration which uses up glucose

Many steady state controls work as feedback systems. A good example of this is the control of the levels of thyroxine in the blood. Low levels of thyroxine cause the anterior lobe of the pituitary to release thyrotropic hormone which stimulates the thyroid gland to produce and release thyroxine. Increasing levels of thyroxine in the blood cause the pituitary to release less thyrotropic hormone. Part of the response (thyroxine) has been fed back to limit the initiating stimulus (thyrotropic hormone).

A much more elaborate series of feedback systems operate during the menstrual cycle in mammals.

THE MENSTRUAL CYCLE:

1) Anterior pituitary produces follicle stimulating hormone, FSH.

2) FSH causes a follicle to grow in the ovary, an egg to mature in it and the follicle produces estrogen.

3) Estrogen feeds back to the pituitary causing a cessation in the output of FSH and a stimulation in the release of luteinizing hormone, LH.

4) Falling concentrations of FSH and rising concentrations of LH causes ovulation, the follicle wall ruptures and releases the mature egg.

Steps 1 to 4 are the follicular stage of menstruation and usually take 10 to 14 days in man.

5) After ovulation the follicle collapses and changes into the corpus luteum. Since FSH production has stopped, estrogen production ceases. LH causes the corpus luteum to produce and release progesterone.

6) Progesterone causes the walls of the uterus to thicken and acquire a rich supply of blood capillaries. This prepares the wall of the uterus for implantation of the egg.

7) If the egg is not fertilized, the egg disintegrates and does not implant.

8) Progesterone from the corpus luteum feeds back and causes the pituitary to cease releasing LH; this causes the corpus luteum to diminish the production of progesterone and to start to degenerate.

9) Falling levels of progesterone cause a breakdown of the special implantation tissue in the uterus. Tissue fragments and blood capillaries break up and are expelled through the vagina. This is menstruation.

Steps 5 to 9 are luteal phase of menstruation and take about 14 days in man.

10) If the egg is fertilized (see step 7) steps 8 and 9 are changed. The fertilized egg implants deep in the special lining of the uterus. The developing embryo and the uterine wall produce a placenta.

11) The placenta produces progesterone, estrogens and other hormones.

12) Placental progesterone maintains the wall of the uterus so it is not discharged.

DISSECTION AND STUDY OF A
HERBACEOUS DICOTYLEDONOUS PLANT

Plants in this category do not produce woody tissue and have two cotyledons (seed leaves) in the seed. Many useful plants occur in this category, e.g. clovers, flax, most vegetables and many greenhouse plants. Dicotyledonous plants are a class in the sub-phylum Angiospermae. These are the most highly developed group — the flowering plants.

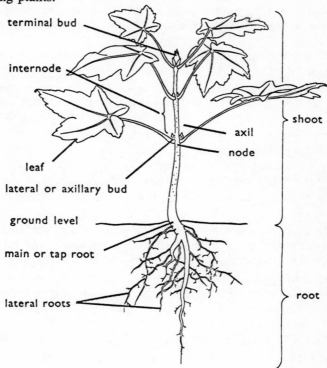

terminal bud
internode
axil
node
shoot
leaf
lateral or axillary bud
ground level
main or tap root
lateral roots
root

42. **Structure of a typical flowering plant.**

SUPPORTING SYSTEMS —

Stems support the structures found above ground and provide orientation of the leaves to light and the spatial arrangement of flowers. Within the stem the conducting system is located. Stems also can store food and water, and contain growth centres (buds) that add both to the height and lateral extent of the stem. The cells in stems are living and obtain a supply of oxygen from the air via openings, stomata or lenticels in their epidermis. Older stems are supported by woody and fibrous tissues which are added layer by layer. Young stems depend for their rigidity on the turgidity of their cells, the cylindrical distribution of their conducting tissues and the opposing stresses of the pith and epidermis.

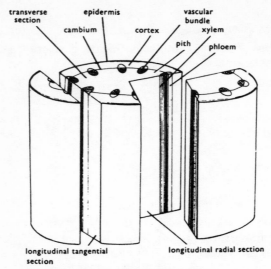

43. Stereogram of plant stem.

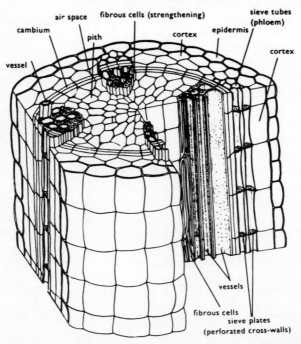

44. Stereogram of plant stem sectioned, showing cells (cell contents not shown).

The Primary Tissues in Stems are as follows:

(a) Epidermis — one layer, transparent, many stomata (see leaves).

(b) Cortex — parenchyma with some modifications:

  1) Collenchyma — just below epidermis, corners of walls thickened; support.

  2) Parenchyma — most of cortex; many cells may have chloroplasts (called chlorenchyma cells) and function in food making; also storage of food.

  3) Starch Sheath (endodermis) — single inner layer of cortex; cells contain many starch grains.

(c) Stele — cylinder inside the cortex.

  1) Pericycle — Several layers of cells on outside.

  2) Vascular Bundles — in stems the xylem and phloem are arranged in vascular bundles (a group of xylem towards the stem centre and a group of phloem towards the outside, on the same radius). In some stems the bundles are in a ring.

  Xylem — contains trachaea, tracheids and parenchyma; also in stem xylem are wood fibres — slender, pointed, dead cells with very thick walls for support; tracheae and tracheids conduct water and minerals up to leaves; tracheids also support, parenchyma stores food.

  Phloem — contains sieve tubes, companion cells and parenchyma (see root); also present usually are bast fibres (sclerenchyma) — long, thick walled, dead cells for support. Sieve tubes and companion cells conduct manufactured food down from the leaves to other parts.

  Cambium — single layer of meristematic cells between xylem and phloem; may produce secondary growth (see later).

  3) Pith — parenchyma cells in centre of stem; storage.

  4) Pith Rays — parenchyma cells between vascular bundles; storage and conduction of food across the stem.

(d) Classification of Primary Permanent Tissues according to Function:

  1) Meristematic (growing) — growing point at end of stem and cambium.

  2) Mechanical (support) — collenchyma; sclerenchyma (bast fibres); tracheids; wood fibres.

  3) Vascular (conducting) — tracheae; tracheids; sieve tubes; companion cells.

  4) Storage — parenchyma.

SECONDARY GROWTH IN DICOTYLEDONOUS STEMS — THE WOODY STEM

All dicotyledon stems when young are similar to that described in the previous section. If the stem is perennial, secondary growth will occur, as follows, and eventually produce a woody stem (shrub or tree).

(a) Parenchyma in pith rays, between cambium layers in bundles, becomes a meristematic to form a complete ring of cambium.

(b) Cambium divides to form secondary xylem towards the centre of the stem and secondary phloem towards the outside.

(c) Secondary xylem develops as annual rings if the growing season varies (spring, summer, winter); rings evident because spring growth is more rapid than summer growth and produces a coarse spring wood with many large tracheae and few wood fibres; summer wood is more compact and has many wood fibres and smaller tracheae. Wood is secondary xylem.

(d) Secondary phloem is produced slowly and remains as a thin layer in inner bark.

(e) Medullary rays (thin sheets of parenchyma cells) are formed in secondary xylem, by cambium, to store and to conduct food across stem from phloem to inner xylem.

(f) Epidermis is replaced by a corky bark as follows: a meristematic cork cambium develops in outer cortex; cork cambium produces cork cells (with waterproof walls) towards the outside; this corky bark protects stem from mechanical injury, insects, bacteria, loss of moisture.

(g) Stomata replaced by lenticels.

(h) Bark consists of cambium, phloem, cortex, cork cambium, and corky bark.

ANCHORING SYSTEMS —

Roots and/or underground stems anchor the plant to the ground. The depth and the form of the root system affect the ability to anchor. Roots of angiosperms can be of two main types:

Tap roots — one deep main root with lateral branches, e.g. dandelion, red clover, they may be fleshy as in the carrot.

Fibrous — numerous fine roots, e.g. most grasses, fibrous roots may also be fleshy as in dahlia or sweet potato.

Proceeding from the growing tip of the root, 4 regions can be recognized:

1) Root cap — brownish protective cap over end of root; loose cell mass replaced as worn off by movement through soil.

2) Growing point — just above cap; meristematic cells which divide to form new cells to lengthen root.

3) Elongation region — about ¼ inch in length; enlargement of cells formed by growing point — causing elongation of root.

4) Root Hair (maturation) zone — this is the absorbing region and also the region in which the parenchyma cells of the elongation region become differentiated to form the specialized tissues (a tissue is a group of cells which have similar structure and do the same kind of work). The cells of these tissues are described in the following section.

Cross Section of Root Hair Zone

Parenchyma cells are generalized cells, regular in shape, thin walls, moderate amount of protoplasm; large vacuoles.

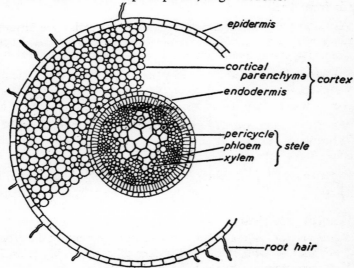

45.   Cross section of root of buttercup, a dicotyledonous plant.

1) Epidermis — single layer, thin walled, root hairs formed as protrusions from epidermal cells; large surface for absorption of soil water containing dissolved minerals and oxygen.

2) **Cortex** — parenchyma cells, spherical, thin walls, large vacuoles; conduction by diffusion of soil water to stele; also storage of food; endodermis is inner thick walled layer of cortex cells.

3) **Stele** — (vascular cylinder)

Pericycle — outer layer of parenchyma cells; capable of division to form branch roots.

Xylem — in dicotyledon in centre of root with radiating spokes; in monocotyledon around a central pith (parenchyma) cylinder. Xylem contains chiefly tracheae and tracheids; tracheids are single cells while tracheae are made from several cells end to end — so are long tubes with large diameter; neither has protoplasm; walls of both are strengthened by thickening of various forms — annular rings, spiral bands, ladder-like bars, or pitted (entire wall thick except for some thin areas); tracheae (vessels) conduct and also support; xylem also contains some parenchyma.

Phloem — between spokes of xylem, contains some parenchyma and sieve tubes and companion cells for conduction of manufactured food downwards. Sieve tube formed from several cells end to end; end walls perforated forming sieve plates; cytoplasm strands extend through sieve plates from cell to cell; companion cells narrow, parallel to sieve tubes; they have dense cytoplasm and may assist sieve tubes in conduction.

Pith — parenchyma cells in centre of monocotyledon root; storage of food.

Root Hairs

Origin — outgrowths from epidermal cells in maturation zone.

Location — extend ½ inch along root just above elongation region.

Structure — white thread ¼ to ¾ inch long; thin walled; contains nucleus of epidermal cell; large vacuole.

Duration — usually a few days — new ones form below as root pushes through soil.

Function — absorb soil water, minerals and oxygen.

Branch Roots — originate from parenchyma cells of pericycle; cells divide to form a growing point (meristematic tissue) which develops a root tip, root tip grows out through cortex and epidermis above elongation region; branching encouraged by adequate mineral supply in soil.

Secondary Thickening in Roots — In monocotyledons and annual dicotyledons the only increase in diameter is due to enlargement of cells. In perennial dicotyledons thickening is due to activity of a new meristematic tissue — the cambium — which develops from parenchyma cells between xylem and phloem. Division of cambium cells forms xylem towards the centre of the stem and phloem towards the outside — the cambium itself soon forming a smooth cylinder; xylem is produced as annual rings of wood; phloem produced slowly and remains as a thin layer; annual rings of xylem are visible because rapid spring growth produces numerous, large thin-walled tracheae which give spring wood and open texture; in old roots a meristematic cork cambium develops, in pericycle, which produces cork cells externally — cortex and epidermis die and root is covered by a corky bark. An old root is very similar in structure to a woody stem.

Root Functions
Primary (General)
1) **Anchorage** — anchors stem which holds leaves, flowers, fruits in suitable positions; depth and form of root system affect ability to anchor.

2) **Absorption** — soil water is a very dilute solution containing minerals useful to plants (chiefly niturates, phosphates and sulphates of potassium, calcium, magnesium and iron); oxygen necessary for respiration in root cells is also present; water and minerals diffuse independently through cytoplasmic membranes of root hairs and epidermal cells; water and carbon dioxide are the only substances in cell sap of root hair vacuoles which can get out through semi-permeable cytoplasmic membranes; no absorption takes place through corky bark of older roots.

3) **Conduction** — Xylem in stele conducts water and minerals up to the stem. Phloem in stele conducts manufactured food down from stem to all parts of root.

Special Functions
1) **Storage** — most roots store much water and food material (starch etc.); fleshy roots (turnip, sweet potato, asparagus, etc.) are especially good for storage; purpose is food supply for next year's growth.

2) **Propagation** — root cuttings of dahlia, sweet potato, etc. produce adventitious buds which reproduce the shoots; stems (suckers) are sent up from adventitious buds on raspberry or lilac roots.

3) **Parasitic roots** — a few angiosperms send special roots into cells of host to absorb manufactured food — dodder on clover and mistletoe on some evergreens.

ABSORBING SYSTEMS —

Root hairs provide the main absorbing region of the plant. The root hairs grow out from the epidermal cells and between the soil particles, their shape therefore being determined, to some extent by the position of the soil particles. Their cell walls stick to the soil particles. This helps keep the soil firm around the roots. The total absorbing area of the millions of root hairs in a root system is very great. The concentration of water in the soil surrounding the root hairs is usually higher than the concentration of water within the root hair cell. Water therefore moves into the root hair cell by osmosis. Inorganic ions dissolved in the soil water can move into the root hair cells by diffusion but the root hair cell can also actively transport certain ions into or out of its cell membrane. *(See Figures 46 and 47)*

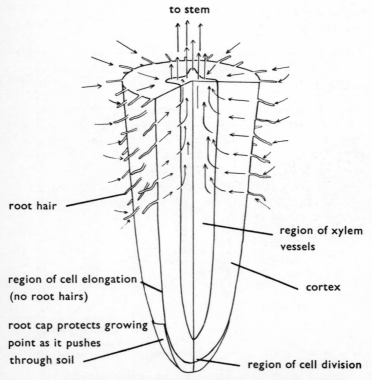

to stem

root hair

region of xylem
vessels

region of cell elongation
(no root hairs)

cortex

root cap protects growing
point as it pushes
through soil

region of cell division

46.   Diagrammatic section of root to show passage of water from the soil.

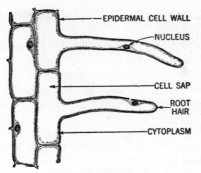

47. Root hairs.

Only 1 to 2 per cent of the water is used in photosynthesis or other metabolic processes; the bulk of the water evaporates from the surface of the leaves, a process known as transpiration.

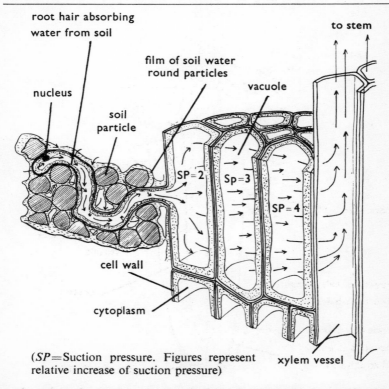

(SP=Suction pressure. Figures represent relative increase of suction pressure)

48. Diagram to show one theory of the passage of water from soil to xylem vessels in a root.

CONDUCTING SYSTEMS —

The mixture of water and dissolved solutes is usually called sap. The vertical movement in plants occurs chiefly in xylem tissue. The best theory to explain the ascent of sap in plants is the cohesion theory. The leaves lose water through transpiration and this causes the leaf cells to be partially dessicated. This lowers the concentration of water in these cells and they tend to pick up water from surrounding cells that have a higher water content. This force is transmitted from cell to cell through the conducting vessels of the leaf and stem downward into the root xylem itself. Thus, transpiration causes a pull to be exerted on the water columns in the xylem. Water molecules tend to stick together and this cohesive force causes the water column in

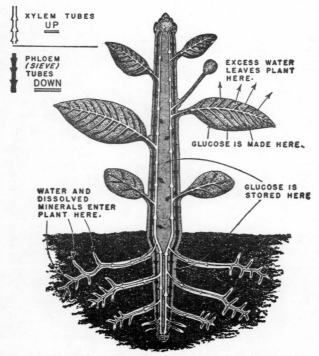

XYLEM TUBES
UP

PHLOEM
(SIEVE)
TUBES
DOWN

EXCESS WATER
LEAVES PLANT
HERE.

GLUCOSE IS MADE HERE.

GLUCOSE IS
STORED HERE

WATER AND
DISSOLVED
MINERALS ENTER
PLANT HERE.

49.   The conducting systems of a green plant.

the xylem to remain unbroken. As one molecule of water is removed by transpiration it is replaced by water molecules moving up the xylem tube. *(See Figure 48)*

Food materials made by the plant, sugars, amino acids, etc., are moved down from the leaves chiefly in the phloem region of the stem, except during the formation of the buds and flowers. This process occurs very rapidly and the exact mechanism of this movement is unknown.

No cell in the plant is far from conducting cells.
(See Figure 49)

GROWTH SYSTEM —

Three kinds of growth are involved in the transformation of a seedling into a plant; growth in length, growth in thickness and branching growth.

1) Growth in length — in root tips and in the teminal buds of shoots there is a region of active cell division, the primary meristem region. When the tip cell divides, one of the daughter cells remains and the other daughter cell is pushed ahead. Behind the growing tip and the zone of division the cells elongate and behind this zone of elongation there is a zone where the cells have begun to specialize.

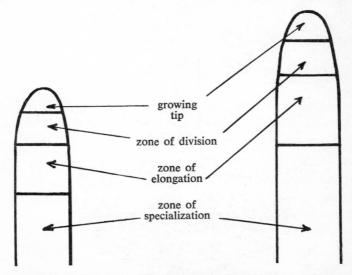

growing
tip

zone of division

zone of
elongation

zone of
specialization

50.   The lengthwise development of a growing shoot, diagrammatic.

2) Growth in thickness — the cambium cells divide frequently and the newly-formed cells are pushed either to the inside or the outside of the cambial tube. This causes an increase in the thickness of the stem.

3) Branching growth — similar to upward growth; the advancing shoot meristem leaves behind patches of embryonic tissues (nodes). Branching growth occurs only at nodes, lateral buds arise here which grow out at an angle to the main stem.

GASEOUS EXCHANGE SYSTEM AND PHOTOSYNTHETIC SYSTEM —

Both these systems occur in the leaves of plants. Figure 51 shows a cross section of a typical leaf.

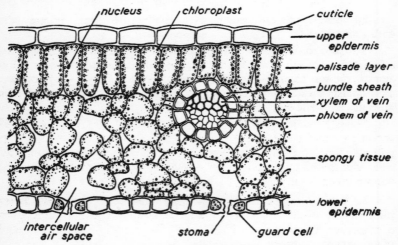

51. Cross section of a portion of a typical leaf, whose blade is supported in a horizontal position.

The following structures can be identified if a cross section of a leaf is examined with a microscope under low power.

1) Epidermis — usually one layer of irregular cells; waxy cutin in outer walls — may have a complete layer covering leaf (cuticle) — this prevents water loss; stomata (average 60,000 per square inch) on lower surface only if blade is horizontal; a stoma is a slit-like opening with a guard cell on each side; guard cells contain chloroplasts; other cells of epidermis are transparent (no chloroplasts); when water supply is good guard cells are turgid and stoma opening is larger — stomata open and close to assist control of water loss (transpiration); guard cells may assist in control of size of stoma.

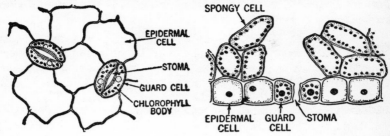

52.   Two views of the lower epidermis of a leaf.

2) Mesophyll (middle leaf) — consists of parenchyma cells with chloroplasts, hence called chlorenchyma.

Palisade tissue — one or more layers of elongated cells side by side just under upper epidermis; many chloroplasts; thin walls; large central vacuole filled with cell sap (water, sugar, CO_2, O_2, minerals); chloroplasts move up and down the cells to secure optimum light intensity for food making.

Spongy tissue — loose mass of irregular chlorenchyma cells between palisade tissue and lower epidermis; fewer chloroplasts than palisade; structure permits connected system of air spaces to reach all cells and permits movement of oxygen, carbon dioxide and water vapour throughout.

3) Veins — contain xylem in upper part and phloem in lower part; bundle sheath cells around outside of vein assist in conduction of sugar out of leaf; some sclerenchyma fibres may be present at edge of phloem for support.

Leaf Functions

1) Gas exchange — all of the cells in a plant, including those in the leaves are continuously respiring. Cellular respiration requires a supply of oxygen and produces carbon dioxide which must be carried away from the cells. In addition to respiration the chloroplast-containing cells, found chiefly in the palisade tissue, photosynthesize. Photosynthesis requires carbon dioxide and produces oxygen which must be carried away from the cells. Both these gases move in and out of the stoma and can diffuse freely in the intercellular air spaces.

2) Photosynthesis — (described in detail previously). The synthesis of glucose from carbon dioxide and water, by chlorophyll-containing cells in the presence of light.

From this simple sugar (glucose — $C_6H_{12}O_6$) the plant can later make other sugars (cane sugar — $C_{12}H_{26}O_{11}$), or starch or fats or proteins. Starch is made immediately after the production of glucose and is found in leaves whenever photosynthesis is going on. Photosynthesis is represented by the following equation —

$$6\ CO_2 + 6\ H_2O + \text{light energy} \longrightarrow C_6H_{12}O_6\ \text{(glucose)} + 6\ O_2 \nearrow$$

The carbon dioxide diffuses through the stomata and into the chlorenchyma cells where the process takes place. The water is obtained by the root and transported up through xylem of root, stem and leaf vein and, if necessary, through air spaces to cells.

Sunlight or other light gets to cells because of transparency of cuticle, epidermis and cell walls. Oxygen released is partly used in respiration and the rest diffuses out through the stomata. The function of chlorophyll seems to be to change the light energy to some form of energy which can perform the synthesis and which then is stored in the sugar produced.

FOOD STORAGE SYSTEMS —

The glucose resulting from photosynthesis can be converted to starch and stored in insoluble starch granules in the cells. The carbon chain of glucose can also be converted into fats, waxes, oils and amino acids. Much of this material is stored in various parts of the plant, in seeds, and such special large storage organs associated with the root system, e.g. carrots, bulbs, corms or rhizomes. Fruits also contain large amounts of stored food.

REPRODUCTIVE SYSTEM —

A flower is a reproductive structure on a plant. Many flowers have both male and female reproductive organs, though some are of a single sex. The floral parts are arranged in whorls and spirals with short internodes, often at the end of a flower stalk whose end is expanded to form a receptacle. The outer whorl is called the calyx, the next the corolla. Within the coralla is the androecium (the male part of the flower) and the gynaecium (the female part of the flower).

1) The calyx — consists of sepals which are small, green leaflike structures. They enclose and protect the rest of the flower while it is in the bud.

2) The corolla — consists of petals which are often coloured and scented; they attract insects which are important agents of cross pollination.

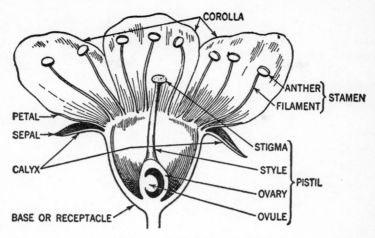

53. A typical flower, diagrammatic.

3) The male part of the flower (the androecium) consists of a ring of stamens. The stalk of the stamen is the filament. At the end of the filament is an anther which contains the pollen grains. The pollen grains contain the male reproductive cells or gametes.

4) The female part of the flower (the gynaecium) consists of carpels which may be (a) single and separate,

(b) many and separate from each other, or

(c) few and joined together.

In all of them the ovule, which contains the female reproductive cells or gametes, is enclosed in a case, the ovary. Extending from the ovary is a style which expands at its end into the stigma. The stigma is the area where pollen will be received. The ovules, when fertilized, will become seeds, while the whole ovary will be the fruit. The wall of the ovary develops into the pericarp of the fruit.

Pollination and Fertilization — When a pollen grain reaches the stimata of a flower, a number of changes take place. The pollen grain contains three nuclei; one of these, the tube nucleus, begins to develop a tube down through the style into the ovary. The other two nuclei are sperm nuclei; they move down the tube as it develops. When the pollen tube reaches the ovule, the tube nucleus breaks down. Only the sperm nuclei enter the ovule.

The ovule in the ovary contains eight nuclei; one of these is the egg nucleus or female gamete. When the two sperm nuclei reach the

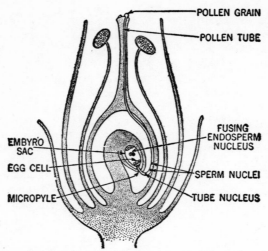

54. Fertilization in the flower, diagrammatic.

ovary, one of them unites with the egg nucleus producing a fertilized egg or zygote. Two of the eight nuclei of the ovule fuse to form an endosperm nucleus which unites with the second sperm nucleus.

The nucleus of the zygote divides many times by mitosis and eventually forms an embryo plant with undeveloped stem, root and leaves.

The fertilized endosperm nucleus also divides many times and forms a large number of cells which surround the embryo plant. These cells store food which is used by the embryo plant when it begins to develop.

The seed is the embryo plant and its food supply with certain protective structures. The fruit is the enlarged ovary with all its contents, including the seeds.

COORDINATING SYSTEM —

Plants lack a nervous system; their growth and development is coordinated by plant hormones called auxins. Auxins have their greatest effect in the primary meristem regions in root tips and shoots. Critical concentrations of auxins cause cells in these regions to elongate. Light affects the production of auxins in plants. If light hits one side of a shoot, the cells on the side away from the light accumulate more auxin and the cells on this dark side elongate, bending the plant towards the light. The exact details of how light causes this effect are, as yet, unknown. Changes in the length of day light (photoperiodism) initiates flowering in many plants. Some plants, e.g. crysanthemums, and soy beans are short-day plants and only flower when exposed to short periods of light. Other plant species, e.g. spinach, flowers only after exposure to long days. Actually the terms short-day and long-day plants are quite misleading because the critical thing is the length of the dark period. Short-day plants are actually long-night plants. If a light is flashed on a short-day plant during its dark period, it will not flower. It seems that light-sensitive chemicals capable of inhibiting flower formation accumulate during the light period; these are broken down during the dark period. Plants differ in their ability to metabolize these chemicals and hence there are short-day (long-night) plants and long-day (short-night) plants.

Fruit development is caused by seeds releasing auxins into the surrounding flower parts which stimulates the growth of fruit.

EXCRETORY SYSTEM —

Carbon dioxide is excreted from leaves through the stomata. Excess metabolic water is removed by transpiration. Some leaves store poisonous metabolic wastes in an insoluble form and they are eliminated from the plant when the leaves fall. Some roots can exude metabolic waste materials into the surrounding soil water.

REGULATION OF THE INTERNAL ENVIRONMENT —

Plants lack the elaborate homeostatic systems found in mammals. Plants do not maintain a high, constant body temperature, but their temperature varies with the environment. The pH of the sap also varies much more than does the pH of mammalian blood. During the day the plant is using carbon dioxide for photosynthesis; this prevents the accumulation of carbonic acid ($CO_2 + H_2O \longrightarrow H_2CO_3$) in the plant sap and conditions are therefore basic. At night however excess carbon dioxide is produced and made into carbonic acid and the sap pH becomes more acid. Acid conditions facilitate the conversion of sugar to starch.

If a plant loses a great deal of water through transpiration the water and salt balance of the plant can be upset, wilting will occur and the osmotic balance in the roots will be affected. Because of the lowering of the concentration of water in the root cells, water will tend to move into these cells from the surrounding soil by osmosis.

CLASSIFICATION OF ORGANISMS

Man has made many attempts to classify plants and animals. He often grouped them on the basis of colour, e.g. all plants with red flowers, all black animals. Another early basis for classification was on the basis of activity, e.g. all flying animals; all animals that swim. These attempts at classification were not very useful because they failed to reveal the evolutionary associations between organisms. Birds, bats and insects fly, and therefore were grouped together in some schemes of classification. An insect however, is not a vertebrate and its wings are formed from a flap of its external skeleton. Insect wings are not modified limbs. The wings of bats and birds are modified limbs. Because they are derived from the same organ, built into the same general plan, and operate in the same general way, these vertebrate wings are homologous structures. Insect wings are derived from a different organ and only work the same way; such structures are said to be analogous.

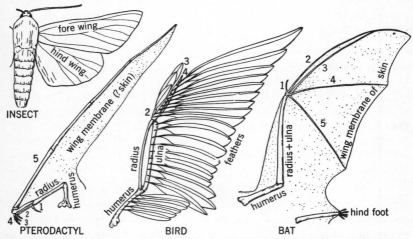

55. ANALOGY between wings of insects (no internal skeleton) and of vertebrates (with skeleton)—of like function but different origins. **HOMOLOGY** in the wing bones of vertebrates, all derived from the common pattern of fore limb in land vertebrates, but variously modified. Pterodactyl (extinct reptile) with very long 5th finger; bird with 1st and 5th lacking. 3rd and 4th partly fused; bat with 2nd to 5th fingers long.

In 1735 a Swedish naturalist, Carl Linnaeus, published Systema Naturae in which he presented a system of classification based on comparisons of homologous structures. Organisms sharing the largest number of homologous structures were grouped together. The true genius of Linnaeus was in his remarkable ability to recognize homologous structures and to grade them in order of importance. In classifying the swimming animals for example, he realized that whales and porpoises were highly modified mammals. Because whales have lungs, breath air, have internal fertilization, are warm blooded, are viviparous and feed their young milk, they are more closely related to cows, mountain lions and men than they are to fish.

Linnaeus was so successful at recognizing homologous structures and grouping animals into their "natural" (actually evolutionary) groups that later work based on evolutionary and genetic studies has done little to change his basic classification.

The real significance of the system of classification developed by Linnaeus became apparent only after Charles Darwin published his theory of evolution in 1859. Darwin recognized that a system of classification based on homologous structures was actually a classification system that showed kinship. Organisms sharing homologous structures are related to one another, having inherited the structure from a common ancestor.

The other major contribution made by Linnaeus to classification was his use of binomial nomenclature in which species are described by two names. Latin names were used by Linnaeus; the first name refers to the genus to which the organism belongs, the second is the specific or species name. Both names are printed in italics, the generic name is capitalized and the specific name is all lower case letters. Roman letters are always used even in countries such as Russia and Japan that have different alphabets. Many species named after Linnaeus do not have true Latin names but simply new words with the generic name made to look like a Latin noun and the specific name in the form of a Latin adjective.

The smallest unit in classification is the species. A species is a population of inter-breeding individuals more or less isolated from all other related and similar populations by either geographic or behavioral barriers. Examples of geographic barriers would be mountains, deserts, rivers and oceans. Examples of behavioral barriers would be differential breeding periods, or courtship patterns. If the breeding periods of organisms do not overlap, there will be no interbreeding even though the two populations of organisms are not isolated geographically. Some animals have an elaborate courtship pattern that they must perform before breeding can take place. Breeding will only occur between individuals that fit into this behavioral pattern and so two populations of rather similar animals with different courtship patterns will not interbreed even though they are not geographically isolated.

This isolation of groups of similar organisms is necessary for maintaining the species. For example, in a zoo, where there may be no isolation, lions and tigers can be interbred, but under natural conditions they are isolated and remain separate species.

Notice that the definition of a species does not refer to individual animals but to a population of similar animals. A population is a relatively permanent grouping of organisms of the same kind. Individual members of a population may leave the population through migration or by dying, but collectively the population remains. Individuals of the same species but of different populations may differ somewhat, e.g. in size and/or colouration. This can happen because individuals from different populations do not interbreed as much as do individuals within their own population. This partial isolation of populations allows some "genetic drift" to occur (see section on evolution).

The next largest unit is the genus which includes all of the related species. Related genera are grouped into families, families into orders, then classes then phyla and finally into either the plant or the animal kingdom.

CLASSIFICATION AND CHARACTERISTICS OF SOME TYPICAL ORGANISMS:

Kingdom	Animalia	— includes all animals
Phylum	Chordata	— animals with notochords or backbones
Class	Mammalia	— body with hair, females give milk
Order	Carnivora	— meat eating animals
Family	Felidae	— all cats
Genus	*Felis*	— includes *Leo* — lion, *Tigris* — tiger
Species	*domesticus*	— house cat
Common name	domestic cat	

Kingdom	Plantae	— includes all plants
Phylum	Tracheophyta	— have conducting tissues

Class	Gymnospermae	— have naked seeds
Order	Coniferales	— have needle-shaped leaves
Family	Pinaceae	— produce female organs that contain a number of ovule-bearing scales
Genus	*Pinus*	— cones mature in two years
Species	*strobus*	— leaves in bundles of 5, the base of the bundles sheathed in small scales
Common name	white pine	

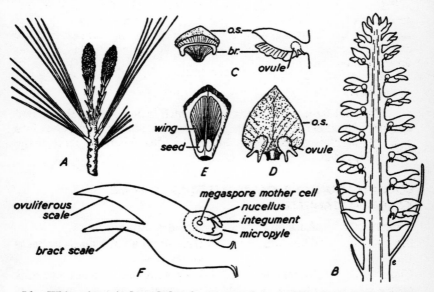

56. **White pine. A, branch bearing two ovulate strobili. B, ovulate strobilus in section showing the arrangement of the megasporophylls. C, megasporophyll, end and side views, o.s., ovuliferous scale, br., bract scale. D, dorsal view of megasporophyll. E, ovuliferous scale with two seeds. F, section of megasporophyll through an ovule.**

Other common pines are *Pinus silvestric,* scotch pine, *Pinus resinosa,* red pine. The spruce trees belong to a different genus, *Picea* and the black spruce is *Picea mariana.*

CLASSIFICATION OF BEETLES TO ORDER:

Kingdom	Animalia	— includes all animals
Phylum	Arthropoda	— joint-footed animals, body typically has head, thorax and abdomen formed of segments. Chitinous exoskeleton covering all parts.
Class	Insecta	— insects, one pair of antennae, head, thorax and abdomen distinct. Thorax typically has 3 pairs of legs and 2 pairs of wings.
Order	Coleoptera	— beetles and weevils — minute to large animals; cuticle heavy; chewing mouth parts; forewings thick and leathery; hind wings membranous; larvae worm-like, usually with three pairs of legs. More than 280,000 species.

CLASSIFICATION OF LEGUMES TO GENUS:

Kingdom	Plantae	— all plants
Phylum	Tracheophyta	— vascular plants
Class	Angiospermae	— with seeds enclosed in ovary
Subclass	Dicotyledonae	— with two cotyledons
Order	Rosales	— a large group; mostly showy flowers; sepals usually united
Family	Leguminosae	— legumes, second largest family of flowering plants, some very common; found in almost every variety of habitat; group includes large trees, climbers, desert plants and water plants. Named after the legume which is its characteristic fruit and almost the only feature constantly found in this large family. Foliage is well developed, large trifoliate, palmate or pinnate, sometimes bipinnate, large stipules. Roots with root-nodules. Inflores-

cence a raceme or head. Three different flower types; flower pentamerous and greatly resembles that of the rose family. Calyx is usually gamosepalous, o f t e n persistent, corolla persistent in some clovers. In the fruit the ventral suture is posterior in position, fruit may curve or even twist in a spiral and may be reduced or fleshy. Seeds large, sometimes kidney - shaped, with thick shiny testa, embryo curved. No endosperm.

Genus	*Mimosa*	— Bipinnate, flower actinomorphic, twice as many stamens as petals, this genus includes the so-called "sensitive plant" that closes its leaves if it is touched.
	Acacia	— Wattle, flower actinomorphic, has more than ten stamens, bipinnate leaves.
	Cassia	— Senna, with purgative pods and *Tamarindus* with edible rounded pods, both have pinnate leaves.
	Astragalus	— Milk vetch, herbaceous, imparipinnate, becomes thorny as leaf blades drop off.
	Robinia	— False acacia, commonly cultivated, tree imparipinnate, thorny stipules.
	Lupinus	— Lupin, palmate leaves adnate stipules, ornamental flowers, leaves stems and seeds used as fodder.
	Ulex	— Gorse, leaves narrow, pointed, simple, small; has sharp, pointed thorns on most branches, no stipules.
	Genista	— Petty whin, leaves simple, has sharp pointed thorns on most branches, no stipules.

Sarothamnus	— Broom, simple and trifoliate leaves on the same plant; reduced stipules.
Trifolium	— Clover or trefoil, stipules adnate.
Medicago	— Medick, like clover but has spiral fruit.
Vicia	— Vetch, a climber, pinnate leaves, terminal leaflet is a tendril, may be branched.
Lathyrus	— Sweet pea, similar to vetch but few or no ordinary leaflets only tendril plus stipules, angular winged stem, ornamental flowers.
Pisum	— Pea, few leaflets, tendrils may be present or absent at end, normal stem. Mediterranean in origin, widely cultivated as a food plant, seeds used alone.
Phaseolus	— Includes scarlet r u n n e r (red flowers), kidney bean, lima or duffin bean, green and black gram. These plants climb by twining their stems, no tendrils, leaves imparipinnate, often trifoliate, small linear bodies at bases of leaflets are called stipels.
Faba	— Broad bean, and *Lens* — lentil, are closely related to *Phaseolus,* the seeds of these plants are used for food.

CHARACTERISTICS OF CERTAIN VERTEBRATE CLASSES:

Class Pisces (Bony Fishes) — skeleton bony; skin usually contains scales; both paired lateral and median fins are usually present supported by bony fin rays; pelvic girdle absent; gills always present, not in separate slits; may have an air bladder; heart has two chambers; small eggs, external fertilization.

Class Amphibia (Frogs, Toads, Salamanders, Newts) — moist glandular skin, no external scales; usually has two pairs of limbs; two nostrils connect to mouth cavity; heart has three chambers, two auricles and one ventricle; breathes using skin, lungs, gills or lining of mouth cavity; fertilization is usually external and eggs are usually laid in water; larvae are usually aquatic and adults are aquatic or are found in moist places on land.

Class Reptilia (Snakes, Lizards, Turtles, Crocodiles, Alligators and Tuatara) — skin dry, usually with horny scales or scutes; usually four limbs each with five toes bearing claws; heart better developed than amphibians, has two auricles and a partly-divided ventricle; cold blooded, breathes with lungs.

Class Aves (Birds) — body covered with feathers; two pairs of limbs, anterior pair modified for flight; warm blooded; four-chambered heart, two auricles and two ventricles, complete double circulation; fertilization internal; oviparous; breathes with lungs.

Class Mammalia (Mammals including Man) — body usually covered with hair; skin contains many glands including mammary glands which produce milk for young; breathes with lungs; heart four-chambered, two auricles and two ventricles; warm blooded; brain well developed especially cerebrum and cerebellum.

CHARACTERISTICS OF THE PHYLUM ARTHROPODA —

Paired jointed appendages with opposing muscles; appendages differentiated for feeding, walking, swimming and as sensory organs; bilaterally symmetrical; segmented body; segments fused into parts to form head, thorax and abdomen; head segments always fused; chitinized exoskeleton; jaws adapted for chewing or sucking, open circulatory system; book lungs or trachea for breathing; excretion by means of green glands or Malpighian tubules; sexes usually separate; fertilization usually internal; one to several larval stages; parthenogenetic development in some crustaceans and insects.

CHARACTERISTICS OF FOUR CLASSES OF ARTHROPODA:

1) Class Myriapoda (Centipedes and Millipedes) — body divided into two parts; one pair of antennae; one pair of mandibles; one or two pairs of maxillae; development direct; has a tracheal system; one pair of legs per segment if centipede, two pairs of legs per segment if millipede.

2) Class Crustacea (Lobsters, Crabs, Barnacles) — chiefly marine but many fresh water species and some that are terrestrial; two body divisions, head and abdomen; respiration by gills; excretion by one or two pairs of green glands; sexes usually separate.

100

3) Class Insecta (Insects) — chiefly terrestrial, some fresh water species, very few marine species; a very large group about 700,000 species; body has three distinct regions, head, thorax and abdomen; three pair of legs; one pair of antennae; wings present in many, absent or reduced in others; development direct in some, incomplete or complete metamorphosis in many; many orders of various forms.

4) Class Arachnida (Spiders, Scorpions, Ticks and Mites) — usually have body in two parts; first pair of appendages modified to form pincer-like structure (chelicerae); two pedipalps; four pairs of walking legs; no mandibles; no antennae; sexes usually separate.

CHARACTERISTICS OF FOUR ORDERS OF INSECTA:

1) Coleoptera (Beetles and Weevils) — minute to large animals; cuticle heavy; chewing mouthparts; forewings thick and leathery; hindwings membranous; larvae worm-like, usually with three pair of legs.

2) Diptera (Flies, Mosquitoes, etc.) — forewings transparent with few veins; hindwings modified to form short knobbed halteres; mouthparts piercing or sponging; larvae usually legless.

3) Hymenoptera (Wasps, Bees and Ants) — mouthparts usually chewing; two pair of wings that interlock in flight or wings absent; female with ovipositor for piercing or stinging; larvae caterpillar-like or legless; complete metamorphosis.

4) Hemiptera (True Bugs) — mouthparts piercing, sucking; pronotum large; triangular plate (scutellum) between wing bases; two pair of wings or wings lacking; forewings thick at base, membranous behind; hindwings membranous and fold under forewings.

CHARACTERISTICS OF FOUR PHYLA OF ALGAE:

1) Cyanophyta (Blue-green algae) — Simplest of all green plants; unicellular; some solitary, other form filaments or ball-like masses.

2) Chlorophyta (Green algae, e.g. pond or water silk — *spirogyra)* — Forms frothy, slippery mass on ponds; each cylindrical cell is independent but hundreds join end to end to form filaments.

One Cell of *Spirogyra*
   i. Cell wall — covered by gelatinous coating, transparent.
   ii. Cytoplasm — thin layer next to wall with strands extending to middle of cell to surround nucleus.

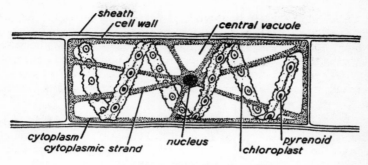

57. **Spirogyra cell, highly magnified.**

iii. Nucleus — at centre (above) — not visible under microscope unless stained.

iv. Chloroplast — may be several in one cell; spiral ribbon in cytoplasm near cell wall.

v. Vacuole — large, central.

vi. Pyrenoids — oval protein and starch bodies in chloroplasts.

Reproduction —

i. Cell Division — asexual — nucleus divides, chloroplast divides and wall forms across cell; end cell divides increasing number of cells in the filament.

ii. Fragmentation — asexual — filament broken by water, animals, etc. — increases number of filaments, each of which grows by cell division.

iii. Conjugation — sexual — usually spring or autumn; occurs between cells of adjacent parallel filaments; projections from opposite cells grow together and form a conjugation tube; contents of one cell (male gamete) flows through tube and fuses with contents of other cell (female gamete); zygote (or zygospore) formed by fusion develops a thick wall and may rest on pond bottom over unsuitable growth conditions; when suitable conditions return zygote germinates to produce a new filament.

(Filaments showing zygotes may be difficult to find — but may be purchased.)

3) Phaeophyta (Brown algae, e.g. rockweed, kelp) — Multicellular; some small and filamentous; others large, growing hundreds of feet in length; may contain one or many gas-filled bladders for buoyancy; a few species float unattached; all but three species are marine.

4) Rhodophyta (Red algae) — Most are marine; typically more delicate and feathery than brown algae; some ribbon-like; a few are free floating; members of the genus *Corallina* accumulate calcium carbonate and help to build reefs.

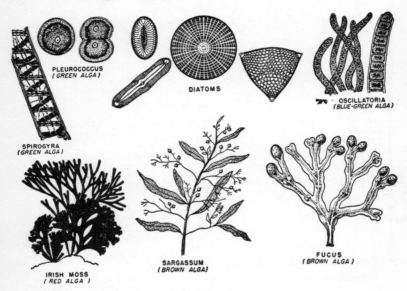

PLEUROCOCCUS
(GREEN ALGA)

DIATOMS

OSCILLATORIA
(BLUE-GREEN ALGA)

SPIROGYRA
(GREEN ALGA)

SARGASSUM
(BROWN ALGA)

FUCUS
(BROWN ALGA)

IRISH MOSS
(RED ALGA)

58. Types of Algae.

CHARACTERISTICS OF FUNGI —

Members of this sub-phylum lack chlorophyll and hence cannot manufacture their own food materials; saprophytic fungi live on dead organic matter; parasitic fungi live on living organisms.

1) Class Phycomycetes (Black bread mould; downy mildews, etc.) — A class in the subphylum Fungi of phylum Thallophyta; plant body or thallus is a long filamentous structure; transverse cell walls may be lacking and so filament appears multinucleate; spores produced in a sporangium.

2) Class Ascomycetes (Mildew, moulds and yeast) — Filamentous septate fungi; reproduction by spores produced in multiples of four in a sac-like ascus or sporangium.

3) Class Basidiomycetes (Mushrooms, puffballs, shelf fungi) — large and conspicuous fungi; the plant body is a mycelium with septate hypae; the visible portion of the higher basidiomycetes is a fleshy

or woody fruiting body; in sexual reproduction the tip of a fertile hypha forms a club-shaped basidium; after nuclear fusion four basidiospores are budded off from the basidium at the tips of short stalks called sterigmata.

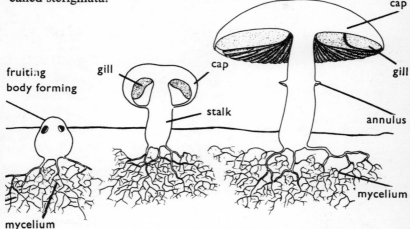

59. Development of the mushroom.

CHARACTERISTICS OF LICHENS —
Found on stones, tree trunks, rock surfaces, etc.

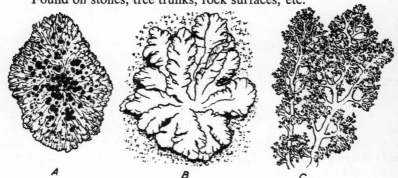

60. Forms of lichens. A, crustose. B, foloise. C, fruiticose.

Types:
  i. Crustose — scale or crust-like.
 ii. Foliose — flat, lobed, leaf-like.
iii. Fruticose — branched.
    Usual colour is grey or greenish grey.

Structure:

   i. Unicellular green alga near upper surface.

  ii. Mesh of fungal hyphae surrounding cells of alga.

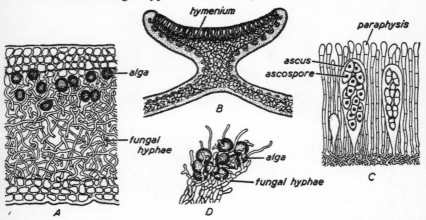

61. Lichen. A, cross section of a thallus. B, cross section of an apothecium. C, section through hymenium of apothecium, showing asci, each with eight 2-celled ascospores, standing among paraphyses. D, a soredium.

  iii. Upper and lower surfaces are cortical layers of tightly woven hyphae.

  iv. Rhizoids consisting of hyphae project from lower surface to attach lichen.

   v. Fruiting cups for spore production by fungus on upper surface.

Symbiotic relationship — these two plants (alga and fungus) live together and are of mutual help.

   i. Alga by photosynthesis makes carbohydrates for both — fungus absorbs from alga cells by diffusion.

  ii. Fungus sponge-like structure holds water for alga.

  iii. Fungus supports and protects alga from drying out, etc.

Importance —

   i. Because of the symbiotic relationship lichens are plant pioneers on bare and exposed rocks where neither alga nor fungus could exist alone.

  ii. Help disintegrate rock and start soil formation.

  iii. Dead lichens and rock particles form first soil by which other plants, usually mosses, first grow. Mosses may be followed by ferns as more soil is produced and finally seed plants.

CHARACTERISTICS OF THE PHYLUM TRACHEOPHYTA —

The phylum includes the ferns, the coniferous trees and the flowering plants; stems contain vascular tissue which act as water conductors (xylem).

1) Class Filicineae (Ferns) — Widely distributed; sporaphyte, has stems and leaves and usually roots, all with vascular tissue; gametophyte in some is brown and tube-like and occurs underground, in other forms it is somewhat flattened, green, fleshy, often lobed or branched.

Habitat — most prefer moist shady locations but a few prefer open uncultivated fields; (obtain in autumn — must dig to get underground rhizomes and roots — may be dried for later use).

Structure and Sexual Reproduction — An alternation of generations is shown as in the moss — here however the sporophyte is the conspicuous generation.

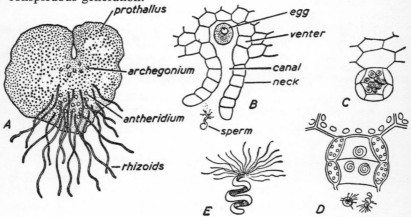

62. Fern gametophyte. A, prothallium, under side, showing rhizoids, antheridia scattered among them, and archegonia near the notch. B, an archegonium; the ventral canal cell and the two neck canal cells have disintegrated and a sperm is shown entering the canal. C and D, antheridia in different stages. E, a sperm.

i. Gametophyte — the tiny (¼ inch) gametophytes (prothallia) may be grown by scattering spores on a moist inverted flower pot covered by a glass jar. Difficult to find in woods. Prothallus is flat, green, somewhat heart-shaped.

Rhizoids — single long cells on underside anchor and absorb.

Antheridia — underside among rhizoids, globular, produce ciliated sperms.

Archegonia — underside near notch, flask-shaped, same parts as moss archegonia, contain eggs.

Usually both sex organs on same gametophyte.

Fertilization — sperm swim to archegonia to fuse with eggs forming zygotes.

ii. Sporophyte — is the conspicuous fern plant. Zygote is first cell of sporophyte. Usually only one zygote grows on a gametophyte. Zygote by cell division produces a mass of cells (embryo sporophyte) part of which (the foot) becomes embedded in prothallus and absorbs food from it until the young sporophyte has developed leaves and roots to support itself. Then the prothallium dies and the sporophyte is independent. Mature sporophyte has a number of parts:

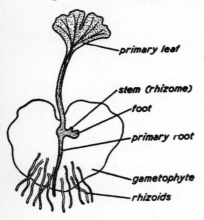

primary leaf

stem (rhizome)

foot

primary root

gametophyte

rhizoids

63. Fern, development of sporophyte.

Rhizome — underground stem, thick, horizontal, perennial, has vascular bundles like stems of seed plants; no aerial stem in most ferns.

Roots — from underside of rhizome, same parts as roots of seed plants (see later section).

Leaves (fronds) — compound with central axis (rachis) and leaflets (pinnae); veins branch by forking, coiled in bud with tip at centre — unroll from base — called circinate vernation; from buds at tip of rhizome.

Sori — rusty spots underside of leaves, consist of spore cases, sporangia and a cover called indusium.

Annulus — ring of cells, with heavy inner wall, around sporangium — straightens in dry weather to open capsule and scatter spores — wind blown. (Spores grow to produce gametophytes.)

As in moss the gametophyte is the haploid phase and the sporophyte is the diploid phase. Change from haploid to diploid is at fertilization and change from diploid to haploid is at reduction division of spore mother cells to produce spores.

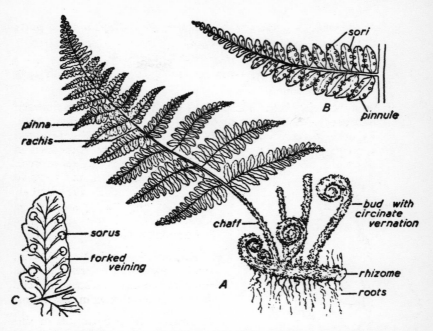

64. **Fern sporophyte. A, a complete sporophyte showing roots, rhizome, and a frond or leaf. B, a pinna enlarged showing sori. C, a pinnule.**

Vegetative Reproduction —

i. Fragmentation of rhizome — older parts of branched rhizome die separating new parts to form distinct plants.

ii. Runners — are produced by some ferns.

2) Class Gymnospermae (Coniferous trees, cycads and ginkgos) — All are woody plants, chiefly trees. The cycads are small and palm-like, resembling tree ferns. The gametophytes are very small; leaves simple, often needle-like. In most the reproductive organs are produced on the surface of the sporophylls which are packed together into cones or strobili (see figure 56). Staminate cones bear the pollen and pistillate cones produce the megaspores and later the seeds.

White Pine as an example of the class Gymnospermae:

Habitat — temperate regions; prefers dry areas since leaves are xerophytic (see later), and stem conducting elements (tracheids) are not suitable for conducting large quantities of water.

Sporophyte characteristics —

    i. Stem — woody perennial; excurrent form (central axis with ring of branches each year producing a cone-shaped tree); wood mostly tracheids (later description) — no vessels or wood fibres; resin canals.

    ii. Leaves — needles; in clusters (2-5); evergreen (last several years); thick cuticle; stomata in pits.

    iii. Root — deep, begins as tap, widely branching.

    iv. Staminate cones (strobili) — one half inch long; in clusters of 10-20; at bases of new shoots; last only two weeks in early June; consist of axis supporting many scales (microsporophylls or stamens); two pollen sacs (microsporangia) on underside of each scale; sacs contain pollen (microspores) with air sacs for wind pollination.

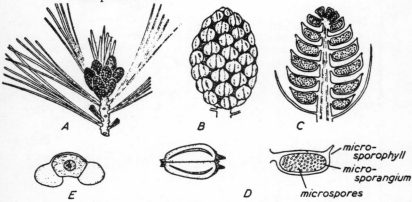

65. **White pine. A, branch bearing many staminate strobili. B, single staminate strobilus. C, longitudinal section of a staminate strobilus showing the arrangement of the microsporophylls. D, microsporophyll viewed from below and in section. E, single pollen grain or microspore much enlarged.**

    v. Ovulate (carpellate) cones — one or two on ends of young shoots; pea-size at first but eventually enlarge to become seed-bearing cones; axis of cone supports double scales — bract scale supports thick megasporophyll with two naked ovules on upper surface; ovule (megasporangium) consists of one integument, nucellus, micropyle, and megaspore (or macrospore). See Figure 56.

Life Cycle

    i. Sporophyte is diploid phase.

ii. Pollen grains (microspores) are haploid — formed by reduction division from microspore mother cells in pollen sacs; consist of tube cell, generative cell, a vegetative cell, and two air sacs.

iii. Pollination — large quantity of pollen; by wind; early June; pollen blown between megasporophylls, which have separated and enters micropyle to surface of nucellus.

iv. Growth of Gametophytes
Ovulate cone, now containing both micro and megaspores, is sealed by resin and hangs downwards.

Female Gametophyte
Megaspore (haploid by reduction division of megaspore mother cells) by cell division forms a many celled megagametophyte containing several simple archegonia each containing an egg.

Male Gametophyte
Tube cell of microspore grows a pollen tube through nucellus into archegonium; generative cell divides to form two sperm nuclei; pollen tube, sperms and vegetative cell make up micro (male) gametophyte. Growth of gametophytes not complete until one year after pollination.

v. Fertilization — one sperm nucleus fuses with egg to form zygote (first cell of diploid sporophyte). Only one egg per ovule is fertilized so ovule produces one seed.

vi. Seed development — zygote by cell divisions forms embryo sporophyte embedded in cellular mass of female gametophyte — this mass is the endosperm (food material for the embryo). Integument becomes seed coat. Embryo contains radicle, hypocotyl, plumule and 3 to 8 cotyledons.

Part of scale becomes attached to seed as a wing for wind dispersal.

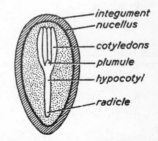

66. White pine seed, in section.

vii. Seed spreading and germination — Ovulate cone enlarges and scales remain closed until seeds mature at end of summer; then scales dry and open to allow seeds to fall out; seeds wind-spread during fall, winter and next summer; usually germinate in spring to form seedling pine tree and finally mature sporophyte. Seed is a dormant embryo sporophyte resistant to temperature extremes and dryness — it may be considered as a ripe ovule. Seed permits dormancy and dispersal. Seed in pine is uncovered — on surface of cone scale.

3) Class Angiospermae (Flowering plants) — Includes most trees and shrubs other than conifers; grains and other grasses; fruits vegetables, garden plants and weeds. Some are woody, others herbaceous; gametophytes microscopic; the ovules are enclosed within ovaries in the carpels of the pistil; pollen tubes grow through the style to the ovule. Some botanists call gymnosperms and angiosperms subphyla.

The Flower —

i. Stamen — is a microsporophyll consisting of filament supporting anther consisting of pollen sacs (microsporangia) containing pollen (microspores).

ii. Pistil — is a megasporophyll — stigma, style and ovary surrounding ovules (megasporangia) containing megaspores. A simple pistil is a carpel.

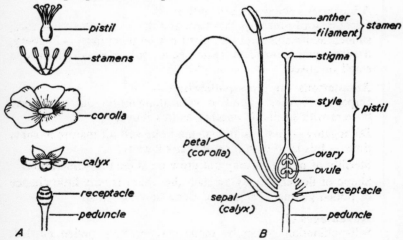

67. The parts of a typical flower. In A, the whorls of flower parts are shown detached from the receptacle and separated. The pistil is formed of fused carpels. B, a vertical section of a typical flower, diagrammatic.

iii. Accessory organs — the perianth consisting of calyx and corolla.

These flower parts are considered to be modified leaves.

Life Cycle —

i. The conspicuous flowering plant is the sporophyte — the diploid phase or generation.

ii. Spores — two kinds as in pine; microspores (pollen) produced in anthers — consist of a cell with tube nucleus and generative nucleus; megaspore — cell in ovule in ovary. Spores, as in pine, are haploid — first cells of gametophytes — formed by reduction division from spore mother cells.

iii. Pollination — transfer of pollen from anther to stigma.

Self-pollination — transfer of pollen from anther to stigma of same flower or a flower on same plant.

Cross-pollination — transfer of pollen from anther to stigma of a flower on a different plant of same species.

Agents of pollination — wind, insects, water.

Adaptations for insect pollination —
Bright colours and odour attract; nectar and pollen are foods for insects; stamens and pistils situated so insects may brush; pollen spiny and sticky; flower may have landing platform, etc.

Adaptations for wind pollination —
Great deal of pollen; pollen light and dry — may have air sacs; stamen and pistils exposed; pistil has large surface — feathery; flowers open before leaves; no nectar, colour or odour; corolla small or absent.

Adaptations for cross-pollination —
Imperfect flowers — flowers with stamens on one plant and flowers with pistils on another as in willow.

Dichogamy — anthers and stigma in flower not mature at same time — this is so with a great many flowers.

Sterility of pollen — may not grow on stigma of same flower.

Shape of flower — may be such that there is very little chance of pollen getting to stigma of same flower — iris.

Advantages of:
Self-pollination — can be made certain; little pollen needed; keeps characteristics pure.

Cross-pollination — stronger seeds produced; some (clover and fruit trees) .develop little fruit if self-pollinated; crossing may strengthen offspring.

Artificial pollination — often used in experiments on heredity. Remove stamens, before maturity, from flower which is going to produce seed; cover this flower; transfer pollen to stigma of this flower from flower on plant that is to be crossed with it; cover flower again till fertilization has taken place; remove cover and allow seed to develop.

iv. Growth of Gametophytes — Megaspore in ovule by division forms 8 nuclei in an embryo sac which constitutes the female (mega) gametophyte — 2 nuclei at centre are the polar nuclei — one nucleus near micropyle is the egg. Ovule with female gametophyte shown is illustrated.

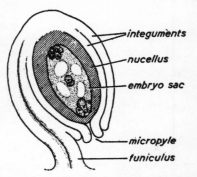

68. An ovule, in longtitudinal section.

Microspore on stigma grows pollen tube down through style into ovule, through micropyle into embryo sac; generative nucleus by this time has divided to form 2 sperms; pollen tube with sperms is male (micro) gametophyte.

v. Fertilization — double fertilization.
One sperm fuses with egg to form zygote.
Second sperm fuses with 2 polar nuclei to form endosperm (triple fusion nucleus).

vi. Seed and Fruit formation —
Zygote by cell division forms embryo sporophyte in seed. Endosperm nucleus by cell division forms endosperm (food material) around embryo in seed. Two integuments of ovule form seed coat (see later for seed structure). The seed (ripened ovule) is enclosed by the ovary which has by this time enlarged. The fruit is the ripened ovary containing the seeds.

SPERMATOPHYTA CHARACTERISTICS —

(also similarities between gymnosperms and angiosperms)
1) Life cycle is an alternation of generations.
2) Specialized structures (flowers or cones) for spore production.
3) Two kinds of spore produced (heterospory).
4) Pollination occurs.

5) Two kinds of gametophyte (male and female).

6) Sperm conducted to egg by pollen tube (water not necessary for fertilization).

7) Sporophyte is the conspicuous generation (diploid phase).

8) Gametophytes (haploid) are much reduced and parasitic upon sporophyte.

9) Seeds (dormant sporophytes) are produced.

Differences between Angiosperms and Gymnosperms —

1) Flower of angiosperm more complex than cone of gymnosperm — perianth added to sporophylls.

2) Ovules of angiosperm enclosed in ovary while ovules of gymnosperm are naked.

3) Pollen grain reaches nucellus in gymnosperm and stigma in angiosperm.

4) Female (mega) gametophyte in angiosperm is much simpler and has no archegonia.

5) Single fertilization in gymnosperm — double fertilization in angiosperm.

6) Endosperm in gymnosperm is remains of female gametophyte and in angiosperm it is developed by cell division of endosperm nucleus.

7) Seeds in angiosperm covered by developed ovary wall forming a structure called the fruit — seeds naked in gymnosperm.

8) Angiosperm seeds have one or two cotyledons — seeds of gymnosperms have three to eight.

Advances of Spermatophytes over Pteridophytes —

1) Sporophyte produces two kinds of spore.

2) Pollination.

3) Gametophytes parasitic on sporophyte and are microscopic.

4) Pollen tube (water not needed for fertilization).

5) Seed produced — advantages of which are:
    (a) Dormancy of sporophyte over poor conditions.
    (b) Dispersal of the plants.
    (c) Food supply for quick growth of embryo.

CONQUEST OF THE LAND BY PLANTS —

The life history characteristics above (last 5 points) combined with the fact that their sporophytes have developed better absorbing, mechanical, and vascular tissues, are the main reasons why the spermatophytes have been able to spread over the earth's surface into almost all kinds of climate and soil conditions. At present the angiosperms with their enclosed, protected seeds make up the dominant land flora, exceeding all other green plants in number of species.

THE INTERDEPENDENCE OF ORGANISMS

All organisms, plant and animal, together with their non-living environments constitute an ecosystem. Within this ecosystem the organisms are interdependent to an astonishing degree. To survive, plants and animals, including man, must adjust themselves to their environment.

The photosynthetic activity and other metabolic activities of green plants produces the energy-rich foods, carbohydrates, amino acids, lipids and vitamins that support directly or indirectly, all other forms of life. One of the most noteworthy features of all living organisms is their extremely high degree of organization. As was pointed out in the section describing cells, protoplasm is not a random mixture of chemicals but a complex, highly organized mosaic.

To describe the state of disorder in any system, the term entropy was coined. Entropy is a numerical measure of disorder. The less probable a given distribution of molecules in a system, the less entropy that system contains. Systems tend to become disorganized, that is to say that the driving force is towards an increase in entropy. Unless energy is supplied, all chemical reactions proceed from a lower to a higher state of entropy.

Living cells proceed from a higher to a lower state of entropy. Cells are constantly taking simple molecules, e.g. amino acids and building them up into very complex, highly organized molecules, e.g. proteins. Because it is working against the force of entropy, cells must constantly be supplied with energy. The energy for all life on earth ultimately comes from the sun. The sun, green plants and animals must all be considered a single system when one considers the thermodynamics of life. Only a small fraction of the energy given off by our sun is trapped by the chlorophyll in green plants, but without this reaction, life as we know it on this planet would be impossible.

The interdependence of organisms is clearly illustrated when one considers the food chains which are commonly found in nature. A typical food chain occurs when small abundant plants, e.g. grass, supports a population of herbivorous animals, e.g. rabbits; these, in turn, serve as food for carnivores, e.g. lynx. The number of lynx are always less than the number of rabbits but the population densities are closely linked. If grass is plentiful and the rabbit population is healthy, its population number will rise. This will mean that food is easily obtained by lynx and this will mean that few lynx will starve to death and the lynx population will rise the next year. Increasing numbers of rabbits will be followed by increasing numbers of lynx the next year. Suppose however, that after three or four good years, disease hits the rabbit population and many of them die. The large numbers of lynx can no longer be fed adequately and so many of them will die. The maximum population size for both the lynx and the rabbits is established by the amount of grass that will grow on the area occupied by the two populations.

In the previous example there is a one-way flow of useful energy. The grass traps the sun's energy with its chlorophyll and uses this energy to make energy-rich molecules, e.g. glucose, amino acids, etc. The rabbits are about 40 per cent efficient in converting the grass they have eaten into their own structure. The lynx would be able to utilize the rabbits that it ate with slightly higher efficiency. At each transfer there is an appreciable loss of energy which is given off in the form of heat.

The chemical elements tend to follow cyclic paths through organisms and the environment, e.g. carbon cycle and nitrogen cycle.

THE CARBON CYCLE —

Carbon dioxide content of air is only about .04% — and this remains constant.

Removed from air by:

Green plants to be used in photosynthesis to make sugar which is changed to starch, cellulose and fats and into proteins by addition of nitrogen compounds and minerals.

Returned to air by:

   i. plant respiration.

  ii. plants eaten by animals followed by animal respiration.

 iii. decomposition of plants by bacteria and fungi.

 iv. decomposition of animals by bacteria.

v. burning of plant materials — wood, coal.

vi. industrial processes such as lime burning.

vii. volcanic gases.

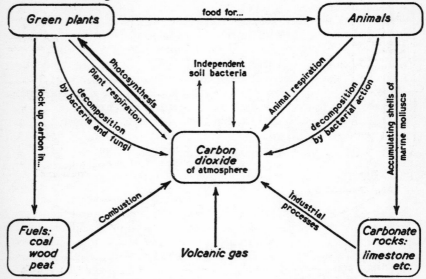

69. Carbon cycle. Carbon finds its way into organic circulation entirely through the photosynthetic process, except for a limited amount through chemosynthetic activity of certain independent soil bacteria.

THE NITROGEN CYCLE —

i. nitrogen in air about 79%, cannot be used directly by plants.

ii. nitrogen to ammonium compounds by fixation.

iii. nitrogen by electrical discharges to oxides which form nitrates in the soil after washing from air by rain.

iv. ammonium compounds in soil to nitrates by nitrifying bacteria.

v. nitrates absorbed by green plants and used to build up proteins.

vi. plant proteins eaten by animals and converted to animal proteins.

vii. decay of plants and animals produces ammonium compounds in the soil.

viii. decay also sets free nitrogen to the air.

ix. denitrifying action frees some nitrogen to the air.

See also the section on amino acid synthesis that occurs in the anabolism section of these notes.

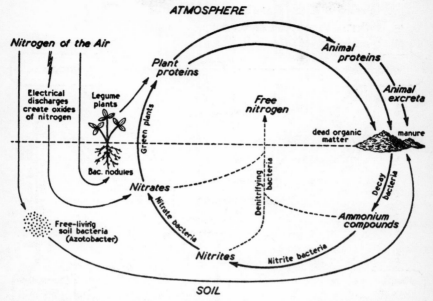

ATMOSPHERE

SOIL

70. Nitrogen cycle. Plants require nitrogen to build the complex proteins of their living protoplasm. Although surrounded by an atmosphere four-fifths nitrogen, most plants cannot use the free gas, but demand nitrogen in chemical combination, mostly in the form of nitrates. Along with other soil solutes, nitrates enter a plant by its roots. Taking this as a starting point, the student should write his own account of the nitrogen cycle. · Note how the action of the denitrifying bacteria is offset by the three agencies at the left that feed atmospheric nitrogen into the organic circulation.

POPULATIONS AND THE OVER-PRODUCTION OF OFFSPRING —

The biotic potential of an organism is its capacity to reproduce and increase its population within a given time. All plants and animals would reproduce at an increasing rate if they were not restricted by limiting factors of the environment. Thus the size of a population at any given time is a ratio of biotic potential to environmental resistance.

Populations tend to grow in a very characteristic way. This can be illustrated by innoculating a test tube full of nutrient broth with a few bacteria. In a few hours there will be millions of cells in the test tube. If population counts were taken at regular intervals during the growing period and the results were plotted on graph paper a very characteristic S-shaped or sigmoid curve would result.

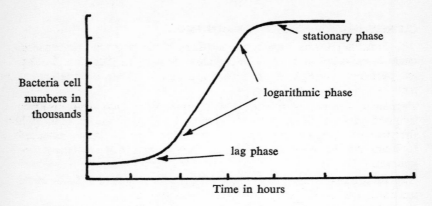

71. Growth of a population of bacteria, a typical population growth curve.

At first the newly-innoculated bacterial cells fail to divide for a time (the lag phase). Then they begin to divide in a rapid and uniform rate, the cells increase in number by a geometric or logarithmic progression, e.g. 2, 4, 8, 16, 32, 64, 128, 256, etc. It can easily be seen that in a very few cycles of reproduction this type of progression can produce extremely high numbers. Eventually the food supply in the culture medium reaches a limit or the waste products released by the organisms reach a high enough level to inhibit reproduction; at this point the reproduction rate gradually slows and the population numbers reach a plateau. Either the organisms no longer reproduce or if they do the death rate matches the reproductive rate and the population number does not change. This is the stationary phase.

The population growth curves of all organisms — protozoa, plants, human beings, are all essentially the same. Such curves can be used to predict the population numbers in various environments. The populations found in a particular habitat are not chance arrangements of organisms. Habitats blend into one another or may be sharply defined, e.g. the edge of the sea.

Biotic communities are constantly changing, this is known as ecological succession. Such changes are usually very slow but can, under certain circumstances, be rapid, e.g. if the community is disrupted by forest fire a rapid succession of temporary communities is established which change until a relatively stable, climax phase is developed.

CLOSELY INTERDEPENDENT ORGANISMS —

Some organisms have increased their biotic potential by forming close association with other organisms. Such organisms are known as: parasites, saprophytes, symbionts, commensals and social organisms.

Parasites — plants or animals which obtain their food from another living species, the host, and give nothing back in exchange. Through the process of evolution successful parasites become highly adapted to living off the host and many of their anatomical structures degenerate.

Saprophytes — plants that absorb liquid organic food from dead materials are called saprophytes, e.g. bacteria, fungi.

Symbionts — "living together", organisms which take food from one another to their mutual benefit, e.g. lichens composed of a fungus which absorbs water and minerals and an algae which photosynthesizes.

Commensals — "feeding at the same table", organisms which associate together and do not harm one another, e.g. pilot fish and sharks, certain hermit crabs and certain sea anemones.

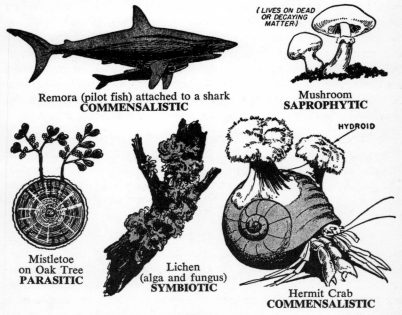

Remora (pilot fish) attached to a shark
COMMENSALISTIC

(LIVES ON DEAD OR DECAYING MATTER.)
Mushroom
SAPROPHYTIC

Mistletoe on Oak Tree
PARASITIC

Lichen (alga and fungus)
SYMBIOTIC

HYDROID

Hermit Crab
COMMENSALISTIC

72. **Dependent Living.**

Social Organisms — species which associate primarily in family groups and in which there is a division of labour between the off-spring and at least one of the parents, e.g. bees, ants, wolf packs, etc.

MAN AS A DOMINANT SPECIES —

Man is the dominant species of animal on this planet. As far as we know he is the only species that is capable of conceptual thought. Man makes tools and machines and has used these to adapt the environment to his needs. Although he can manipulate it to an astonishing degree, man is still dependent on the ecosystem of this planet. He has increased his population size primarily by controlling diseases and reducing the death rate.

Using conservative figures the human population of the world has been estimated as follows:

Year	World Population in millions	Percentage Growth
1650	550	30%
1750	728	60%
1850	1171	over 100%
1950	2400	
1960	3000	over 100%
1980	5000	

Not only are the total numbers going up at a fantastic rate, the actual rate of increase is accelerating. It is estimated that the population of the world will more than double itself in the next 30 years!

The rapidly growing population, especially in the economically underdeveloped areas of the world is the most important biological problem facing mankind. According to United Nations figures, over half of the world's peoples today are suffering from malnutrition.

As man's numbers increase and we proceed towards a more highly industrialized civilization, we use up essential and non-replaceable metals and fossil fuels; we pollute our environment at a time when increasing amounts of fresh water are required.

If man is to preserve his well-being on this planet, he must learn to balance his biotic potential with the ecological limits of this planet.

REPRODUCTION IN PLANTS AND ANIMALS

Reproduction is the ability of an organism to give rise to a new individual. The process of reproduction occurs in many ways, however all of these methods fall into two general categories:

1. — Asexual or vegetative reproduction.
2. — Sexual or gametic reproduction.

ASEXUAL REPRODUCTION —

No special reproductive cells or gametes are involved, a part of the parent organism dissociates itself and develops into a new individual. There are four types of asexual reproduction. In the first two types, binary and multiple fission, the entire structure of the parent cell is the reproductive unit, all of its structure goes into the daughter cells. In the second two types of asexual reproduction, fragmentation and budding, only a part of the structure of the parent is involved in producing the offspring.

Types of Asexual Reproduction —

1) **Binary Fission** — actually this is identical to mitotic division (see mitosis description earlier in these notes). The parent cell doubles its DNA genetic information and then splits into two daughter cells each containing a complete set of the DNA genetic information.

2) **Multiple Fission** — the nucleus of the parent cell goes through several mitotic divisions, the DNA genetic information is duplicated at each nuclear division and each daughter nucleus contains the same genetic information. During this process the cytoplasm has not divided. When the cytoplasm does divide it forms many smaller cells, each containing one nucleus. This type of asexual reproduction occurs primarily in protozoa.

3) **Fragmentation** — a small part of the parent body pinches off and then each piece regenerates the parts that it lacks, e.g. sea anemones and flat worms occasionally break into two units and each then develops into a complete animal. Artificial fragmentation can result among many species of animals and plants. If a piece of a plant such as a geranium or a rose is cut from the parent plant and placed in wet sand or water, the cutting will regenerate a complete plant. Pieces of animals, such as starfish, worms, sponges, etc., will regenerate entire new organisms.

4) **Budding** — a small portion of the body of the organism grows outward and develops into a complete new organism. The young organism may then detach itself from the the parent or it may remain

permanently attached and after maturing it may produce buds of its own. This type of development can lead to large colonies of attached animals. Budding occurs primarily in animals that do not move about much, e.g. sponges, colenterates, flat worms and yeast.

Asexual reproduction has several advantageous features for animals that move about very little. No contact with another animal or plant is required and specialized tissues for reproduction are not required.

Man has capitalized on the ability of plants to reproduce asexually by vegetative reproduction. By planting cuttings and by grafting one type of plant onto another, seedless fruits which could not reproduce sexually can be propagated.

In all of these types of asexual reproduction there is no mechanism for changing the DNA genetic information. Each offspring carries the same genetic code as did the parent.

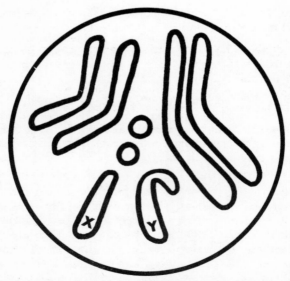

73. The chromosomes of *Drosophila* diploid 2N number is eight. The sizes, shapes and number of the chromosomes in any species is fixed. The X and Y chromosomes which are not a pair, determine the sex of this animal. The chromosomes are described as 1 pair of small boomerangs, 1 pair of large boomerangs, 1 pair of dots and a pair of X chromosomes if female; and an X and a Y chromosome if male.

SEXUAL REPRODUCTION —

In this type of reproduction special male reproductive cells (sperm) unite with special female reproductive cells (egg) to form a zygote which develops into a new individual. The most important point in this type of reproduction, as far as evolution is concerned, is that part of the DNA genetic information comes from the male and part from the female. There can be a slight redistribution of the DNA genetic code and this can lead to variability among the offspring. The reproductive cells (gametes) are produced by a special type of cell division known as meiosis. The most important feature of this type of cell division is that the normal number of chromosomes, which is actually 2N number of pairs of chromosomes, is reduced to half that number. Each gamete receives one complete set of chromosomes. The fruit fly *Drosophila melanogaster,* one of the experimental animals used in the study of genetics, is a good animal to use as an example. The body cells of *Drosophila* contain eight chromosomes, actually 4 sets of paired chromosomes. The chromosomes in *Drosophila* have definite shapes as shown in Figure 73.

Figure 74 shows what happens to the chromosomes during mitotic and meiotic cell division in *Drosophila.*

Each diploid (2N) cell received one set of chromosomes from the female parent, through the egg. These are the maternal chromosomes and are indicated in black. The other set of chromosomes was received from the male parent through the sperm. These are the paternal chromosomes and they are indicated in white.

The important thing to notice in Figure 74 is that the daughter cells produced by mitosis have the same number and colour of chromosomes as did the parent cell. In meiotic division each mature gamete has one complete set of chromosomes but there is a random distribution of maternal and paternal chromosomes in any given sperm or egg. The mechanism that introduces this variability is the way the pairs of chromosomes line up during the metaphase of the first meiotic division. Instead of lining up in one straight line as they do in mitosis the chromosomes line up in pairs. The maternal or paternal chromosome of any given pair can be on the left or on the right. In an organism like *Drosophila* which has a diploid number of eight there are sixteen different combinations of maternal and paternal chromosome sets that can line up on the left or the right at this stage in meiotic division. This means that after the second meiotic division there are sixteen possible assortments of maternal

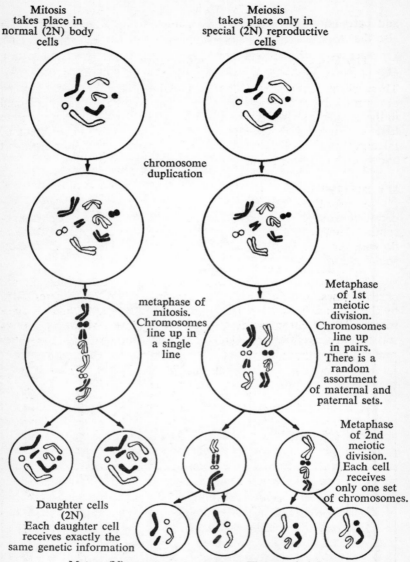

Mitosis
takes place in
normal (2N) body
cells

Meiosis
takes place only in
special (2N) reproductive
cells

chromosome
duplication

metaphase of
mitosis.
Chromosomes
line up in
a single
line

Metaphase
of 1st
meiotic
division.
Chromosomes
line up
in pairs.
There is a
random
assortment
of maternal and
paternal sets.

Metaphase
of 2nd
meiotic
division.
Each cell
receives
only one set
of chromosomes.

Daughter cells
(2N)
Each daughter cell
receives exactly the
same genetic information

Mature (N) gametes, sperm or egg. The genetic information in
the gametes is not identical because of the random assortment of
the maternal and paternal chromosomes during the metaphase
of the 1st meiotic division.

**74. A comparison of mitosis and meiosis in *Drosophila* which has a
diploid (2N) number of 8.**

and paternal chromosomes in the gametes (see Figure 75). Note also that each gamete gets one complete set of chromosomes.

The DNA encoded genetic information on each member of a pair of chromosomes is highly similar but slight differences can occur. These slight differences can play a major role in pre-adapting an organism for evolutionary selection. This will be further explained in the section on genetics and evolution. The important thing to note here is that sexual reproduction allows a random reassortment of maternal and paternal sets of chromosomes. This rearrangement allows each offspring to differ slightly from its parents.

SEX DETERMINATION —

Some of the chromosomes in cells determine which sex the organism will be. These chromosomes are the sex determining chromosomes. They may also carry genetic information that has nothing to do with sex determination. The other chromosomes are called autosomal chromosomes.

In *Drosophila* males have an X and a Y arrangement of sex chromosomes, and the female XX. In this species sex is determined by the balance between X chromosomes and the autosomal chromosomes. The Y chromosome is relatively inactive. Males have three sets of autosomes working against one X chromosome. Females have

75. All the possible arrangements of maternal and paternal chromosomes in gametes of an organism with a diploid number of eight, e.g. *Drosophila*, black, maternal white, paternal chromosomes.

2X chromosomes and this is enough to overcome the autosomal effect which produces maleness.

In man and most other mammals the Y chromosome is active and it contributes to maleness. Males have the XY arrangement and females XX. Sex determining genes are located on all of the chromosomes in man however.

Since male cells in both man and *Drosophila* have the XY arrangement, when sperm is produced half the sperm will have the X part of the pair and half the Y chromosome. Females which are XX will only produce X type eggs. If a sperm carrying the Y chromosome fertilizes an egg the XY arrangement is established and the zygote will be male. If the egg is fertilized by an X bearing sperm a female will result.

HEREDITY

Chromosomes were described earlier in these notes as long double-stranded chains of DNA surrounded by protein. A gene was defined as enough DNA information to describe a protein molecule. The chromosomes carry the genes and the behavior of the chromosomes, which are visible, can be used to describe how the genes are moved about during cell division. Thus from the behavior of the chromosomes during meiosis it can be deduced that genes occur in pairs, one on each of a pair of chromosomes. Genes segregate at random, depending on how the chromosomes line up during the first metaphase of meiosis. Genes are arranged in linear order on the chromosome. Genes which are located on the same place on a pair of chromosomes are called alleles. They usually differ in their ability to produce a trait — one gene may be dominant and the other recessive. If the two alleles are the same the organism is homozygous for that characteristic. If the alleles differ the organism is said to be heterozygous for that characteristic.

Monohybrid cross — In pea plants a plant homozygous for the tall characteristic has the alleles TT. A homozygous dwarf plant is tt. Tallness dominates dwarfness so a heterozygous Tt plant is tall. If a TT is crossed with a tt, one gets the following result:

```
              male              female
              TT        X        tt
gametes  —   T   T              t   t
```

possible recombinations — as male pollen will all be T type and the female gametes all t type, the results will be Tt and all of these plants will be tall. If these Tt plants are cross bred however, one gets different results.

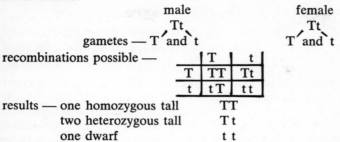

results — one homozygous tall   TT
      two heterozygous tall   T t
      one dwarf   t t

Crosses involving many genes can be worked out in this same way. Note especially however how gamete production by meiosis allows the genes to segregate at random.

Genes do not always act by themselves; some genes work with others to produce a multi-gene effect, — skin colour and height in man are some examples of multi-gene traits.

Linkage — Genes in one chromosome tend to be inherited as a group; all genes on one chromosome are linked; chromosomes rather than genes assort independently during meiosis.

Sex-linkage — Some genes are located on the sex chromosomes and are inherited with sex. For example, haemophylia, a condition in which the blood does not clot is located on the X chromosome in man. It is a recessive gene and is completely masked in the heterozygous condition. Suppose a normal male is crossed with a heterozygous female: (normal gene XB, recessive gene Xb.)

	male	X	female	
	XB Y		XB Xb	

gametes — XB and Y   gametes — XB and Xb

possible recombinations —

	XB	Xb
XB	[1]XBXB	[2]XBXb
Y	[3]Y XB	[4]YXb

the results are:

1) a normal homozygous dominant female
2) a normal heterozygous female
3) a normal male
4) a haemophyliac male

Eye colour in *Drosophila* is similarly sex-linked.

Crossing over — linkage is usually not complete during meiosis. Pairs of chromosomes may exchange parts. This may give rise to new gene combinations. These new combinations may improve the organism's biotic potential or they may be a disadvantage.

Mutations — changes in the DNA genetic information. Such changes may occur naturally or they can be caused by ionizing radiation or certain chemicals. Mutations provide new genetic information. Two types of mutation occur:

1. — Gene mutation — a change in the DNA of a single gene. Different genes vary in their ability to mutate.

2. — Chromosomal mutation — changes in chromosomal number or chromosomal structure. One of the results may be that the normal dilpoid number is increased, a condition known as polyploidy.

Organisms inherit genes, not traits. The gene must function in a normal environment to show its normal effect. A person with a set of genes that would allow him to grow tall will not reach his maximum height if he is not adequately provided with nutrients during his developmental period. The most dramatic period to study the interaction of genes is during the very early development of an organism when its life is just starting.

THE CONTROL OF DEVELOPMENT —

After the sperm has fertilized the egg the resulting zygote consists of a single cell with the diploid 2N number of chromosomes that is characteristic of its species. Soon after fertilization a number of mitotic divisions or cleavages take place. These are cell divisions which are not accompanied by much growth. The result of these cleavages is a ball of cells called a morula. The inner cells of the morula then migrate to the surface and form a hollow ball of cells, a blastula. Soon, after repeated cell divisions accompanied by cell growth, part of the wall of the blastula folds in. This infolding gives rise to a two-layered structure the gastrula (see Figure 76). The inner cell layer is the endoderm, the outer layer the ectoderm. Later a third layer of cells forms between the endoderm and the ectoderm — this middle layer is the mesoderm. Figure 76 lists the various structures that develop from these three primary layers.

SUCCESSIVE CELL DIVISION

	EPIDERMIS
ECTODERM	BRAIN
	NERVES

	MUSCLES
	BONES
MESODERM	RESPIRATORY SYSTEM
	CIRCULATORY SYSTEM
	EXCRETORY SYSTEM

	DIGESTIVE SYSTEM
ENDODERM	LINING OF RESPIRATORY
	SYSTEM AND
	ALIMENTARY CANAL

BLASTULA   GASTRULA BEGINNING   GASTRULA COMPLETE

76. Embryological development of vertebrate animal.

The growth in cell numbers during this development was through mitotic cell division. In mitotic cell division each cell receives exactly the same DNA-encoded genetic information. This means that each cell resulting from mitotic division has the complete description of the entire organism. Obviously each cell uses only part of its DNA-encoded information; liver cells use only those genes which enable them to function as normal liver cells; similarly nerve cells and kidney tubule cells only have some of their genes activated.

What activates the different genes in the different cells? How is development controlled? The simplest answer is that cells in an organism are constantly trading molecules, some of these molecules have the ability to activate or deactivate genes. As the organism develops, cells which will become liver cells start to receive molecules that turn on their "liver cell" genes. As one moves away from the region in the embryo where the liver will develop, fewer and fewer of these molecules that will activate "liver cell" genes are found but more and more of other molecules with the ability to activate other sets of genes. Embryologists have shown that development is controlled in this way through a series of ingenious experiments. If tissues on a developing embryo are moved into unnatural locations they still have the ability to activate certain genes. For example if the eye cup of a developing embryo is transplanted just below the skin in the belly region of an amphibian, the eye cup cells will release molecules that will turn on the "lens making" genes in the epidermal cells. This will induce the epidermal cells, which would normally have produced skin cells, to turn off the "skin cell" genes and to turn on "lens making" genes.

Development is controlled therefore by activating or deactivating parts of the genetic information. Development is therefore ultimately under genetic control, genes which are absent cannot be activated!

At some time, usually quite late, during embryonic development certain cells are set apart as the primary reproductive cells. These are the cells that will divide by meiosis, not mitosis, and will produce the haploid, N, gametes. All of the rest of the body cells are produced by mitosis.

After embryonic development the young organism is born if it is a mammal, hatches if it is a bird, fish or amphibian, breaks through the ground if it is a plant. The organism then goes through the process of maturing, reproducing and eventually, dying. For any given species to persist, its birth rate must match its death rate. Various mechanisms have evolved which help populations of organisms to maintain their population numbers. Organisms which reproduce asexually can maintain their numbers without requiring access to a member of the opposite sex. This is an obvious advantage to organisms that do not move about. Sexual reproduction, on the other hand, allows the organism to produce individuals with genetic information that differs slightly from its parents. This may allow the individual to take better advantage of its environment than its parents and consequently to increase its biotic potential. Some plants and animals maintain their population numbers by producing enormous numbers of seeds or eggs. The animal kingdom has evolved another mechanism for maintaining its populations. Certain animals protect and care for their young. Mammals are particularly noteworthy in this respect. Young mammals usually have a long association with one or both parents. The parents protect the young and in so doing maintain their population numbers.

EVOLUTION

The theory of evolution was effectively presented to the world in 1859 by Charles Darwin when he published his book the "Origin of Species". Darwin based his theory on many years of observation made all over the world. The theory, as proposed by Darwin, rested on five principles.

1. All species exhibit structural and functional variation. These affect the chances of survival.

2. Each species has a great potential rate of increase, that if unchecked, would exhaust its food and living space.

3. Those individual organisms having advantageous variations will survive the struggle for food and living space.

4. Constant selection (natural selection) of better adapted individuals and the elimination of less well adapted ones, results in evolutionary change.

5. The qualities that promote survival are passed on from generation to generation.

The theory of evolution states that the present species have descended, with modifications, from species that existed in the past. Species are not fixed, unchanging things, but are constantly evolving. Evolution is therefore the constant change that has occurred in our world since its beginning to the present time.

When first published, Darwin's book was subjected to a great deal of criticism by people who were convinced, on religious grounds, that species could not change and consequently one species could not evolve into another.

Darwin published at a time when practically nothing was known about genetics and consequently he could not explain the basis for the "variation" he found in plants and animals. Since that time the findings of genetics have been incorporated into the theory of evolution. This more up-to-date theory is called neo-Darwinian evolution. It is based on Darwin's principles of variation, over-production of offspring and natural selection, but variations are interpreted on the basis of modern genetic concepts (gene theory and population genetics). These modern concepts have added to the understanding of the mechanisms of evolution but have not changed Darwin's basic theory.

EVIDENCE THAT EVOLUTION HAS TAKEN PLACE —

The facts to support the concept of continuous change come from many sources, geology, anatomy, embryology, paleontology, genetics, biochemistry, etc.

1) **Geological evidence** — measurements and analyses of rocks and rock formations (silting rates, radioactive dating, salt deposition, etc.) indicate that the earth is about five thousand million (5 billion) years old. The first life appeared only one and a half to two billion years ago. The first good record of living material preserved in rock (fossils) is from the Paleozoic era about 540 million years ago. By this time almost all the phyla were already in existence. By tracing fossil remains that appear in rock strata laid down during

later time periods a progression of forms can be seen. The invertebrates gradually are modified until a vertebrate form appears. In later strata the fishes predominate but modifications can be seen that gave rise to the amphibians, some amphibians in still later strata show modifications that eventually gave rise to the reptiles. The reptiles in turn, gave rise to the birds and the mammals. There is good fossil evidence to support this progression of forms.

2) Anatomical evidence — The classification of organisms is based on the comparison of homologous structures (see section on classification in these notes). Closely related forms have many similar anatomical features. Vestigial structures, usually much reduced and lacking any apparent function are found, e.g. the appendix and the muscles at the base of the ear in man, these are left-overs from an ancestral species in which these structures were functional.

3) Embryological evidence — The embryological developments of all vertebrate animals is extremely similar. This is explained in the theory of evolution. The vertebrates continue to pass through many of the embryonic stages that ancestor species passed through because the developmental mechanisms were inherited from a common ancestor. This would explain why gill slits similar to those found in fish embryos appear temporarily during the development of the human embryo. Other primitive features that appear and disappear during the development of the human embryo are a tail and a two-chambered heart. If we have evolved through the fish-amphibian-reptile-mammal line, the appearance of these structures which are persistent parts of the fish, amphibian and reptile embryos is not too surprising.

4) Physiological evidence — The tremendous unity shown by all living things supports the theory that says that living things evolved from common ancestors. All life, as we know it, runs on a similar series of biochemical reactions, the chemicals found in the protoplasm of plants and animals is extremely similar. DNA and RNA are similar in plants and animals as are the processes of mitosis and meiosis.

5) Biogeographical evidence — Geographic distribution first started Darwin thinking of the possibility of an evolutionary origin of species. He noted how closely allied animals replaced one another in the various ecosystems that he studied as he went from one continental area to another. On the Galapagos Islands, situated 600 miles west of Ecuador, Darwin discovered 13 different species of finch. All of these were basically alike although they differed in size, plumage and beak shape. They were however, true species and did not inter-breed. Darwin postulated that since there were no similar birds on the island to form competition for the finches, the initial finch population evolved to fill ecological niches which would be held, under normal conditions, by other species of birds. This is an example of divergent evolution.

THE MECHANISM OF EVOLUTION —

The unit of evolution is the species population and the mechanism for change is natural selection acting on the inheritable variations in a population. Inheritable variations can arise in two ways: by sexual recombination (see section on meiosis) or by mutation. In each generation some individuals in a population will have some new DNA-encoded genetic information. If these slightly changed individuals can survive and reproduce, this new genetic information will remain in the population and may spread. If the new genetic information increases the biotic potential of the organisms that have it, these organisms will produce more offspring than the originals and eventually the new genetic information will spread throughout the population. Let us take DDT resistance in the housefly as an example of the way the mechanisms of evolution work. If a population of houseflies is sprayed with DDT most of the individuals in the population will die. The survivors live because they have genetic information that the susceptible flies lack. The resistance to DDT is due to the fact that the surviving flies have a gene that produces an enzyme, DDT dehydrochlorinase, that changes DDT to a less toxic product DDE. This gene is located on one of the autosomal chromosomes and it is dominant over the normal allel.

Under normal conditions houseflies never come in contact with DDT. The fact that certain members of the housefly population had been pre-adapted to be able to exist in environments where DDT was present was completely by chance. Organisms do not change their genetic information so that they can exist in new environments — the mechanism of evolution works the other way. Organisms are constantly changing their DNA-encoded genetic information through the mechanisms of sexual recombination and mutation. These changes are not brought about by environmental needs. If the environment changes and natural selection makes new demands on a population some individuals in the population may be pre-adapted to take advantage of the change in which case they will survive and pass their beneficial genes on to their offspring.

In the case of the houseflies and DDT resistance, the selection forces were extreme and very rapid. In most cases the selection works slowly over long periods of time. All that is required for a genetic change to spread through a population is that the genetic change increases the biotic potential of the individuals that have it in comparison to the individuals that do not.

One of the most common selective mechanisms that leads to the development of new species is geographic isolation. Darwin's finches on the Galapagos Islands are a good example of this. The original finch population was probably carried out to the islands by a storm. Once there they were isolated genetically from the mainland finches. As the finches on the island increased in number there would be competition for food. Any change in the genes which would allow individuals to take advantage of other food, e.g. mutations that changed the shape of the beak from a seed eating shape to a parrot-like, fruit eating shape, would be an advantage. Gradually there would be an accumulation of genetic changes until finally the genetic difference would be so great that the two divergent groups would no longer interbreed. In this way a new species would have evolved.

As well as divergent evolution, as seen in Darwin's finches, there is also convergent evolution, as seen in animals that live in the sea. To successfully live in the sea an animal must have a stream-lined fish-like shape. Whales, seals and porpoises are mammals that have evolved from land-living ancestors. The reason that they all have a fish-like shape is because the environment that they live in demands it. Creatures that are shaped like fish can move more easily through water than can bulky, non-streamlined ones. Natural selection for efficiency of movement would favour animals that had, by chance, acquired the genetic information to build a streamlined body. Such animals would have a higher biological potential than bulky animals and so the animals with less efficient shapes would gradually be replaced by their more efficient relatives. Convergent evolution produces animals that look similar even though they come from completely different sources.

Man has made use of the plasticity of species to produce special domestic animals and plants. Instead of nature doing the selection man does it. Even before he knew anything about genetics, primitive man was manipulating the selection of plants and animals. It was common knowledge in ancient Egypt, for example, that strong, high-yielding animals and plants produced similar characteristics in their offspring. When the knowledge gained through the study of genetics became available, the plant and animal breeders were able to do surprising things. It is possible for a plant breeder to "custom make" a plant to order. A major soup company recently wanted a special type of tomato. They specified the colour, skin thickness, size, speed of growth and the acidity of the contents of the tomato fruit. In one or two seasons of cross breeding and selecting, the plant breeders had produced exactly the fruit that was required.

Man can introduce chemicals and ionizing radiation into the environment of a plant or an animal that will increase the rate of mutation. He also can select desirable traits that arise, with remarkable skill and speed. He has not yet been able to manipulate and change the genes exactly as he wishes. Desirable mutations still must arise by chance and the organism must be pre-adapted before either natural or human selection takes place.

The theory of evolution is the major contribution that the biological sciences have made to man's philosophy. Evolutionary thinking permeates every facet of our daily lives. It is most important therefore that the mechanisms and course of biological evolution be clearly understood.

NOTES

NOTES

NOTES

NOTES

NOTES

NOTES

NOTES